TECHNOLOGICAL CHANGE AND THE CITY

Editor:

Patrick N Troy

The Federation Press
1995

Acknowledgments

We gratefully acknowledge the work of the late Bill Mitchell and thank his wife Mrs Rhonda Mitchell for her kind permission to use Bill's cartoon which appears in Chapter 5 of this volume. We would also like to acknowledge *The Australian*, in which this cartoon originally appeared.

It is said that every book, including those which are sole authored, is the product of cooperation and collaboration between a number of people; this is no different. This work is clearly the result of a collaborative effort between all the authors who engaged in a rigorous exchange over a two year period. Their labours were reviewed by peers from throughout Australia who engaged in a debate over chapter drafts and generously offered criticism, both anonymous and public, and to whom we acknowledge our debt. The work would not have been translated to its present form but for the energy, professionalism and commitment of Glenys Harding and Rita Coles, who with good humour, insight and the precise degree of goading which forces one to discharge one's obligations to contributors, referees and publishers made me bring the project to a conclusion. Any strengths the book has should be attributed to them, I accept responsibility for its weaknesses.

Published in Sydney by:
The Federation Press
PO Box 45, Annandale, NSW, 2038.
3/56-72 John St, Leichhardt, NSW, 2040.
Ph (02) 552 2200. Fax (02) 552 1681.

National Library of Australia
Cataloguing-in-Publication entry

Technological change and the city.

    Bibliography
    Includes index.
    ISBN 1 86287 184 1

    1. Cities and towns - Effect of technological innovations on - Australia 2. Municipal services - Australia. 3. City planning - Australia. I. Troy, Patrick N. (Patrick Nicol).

307.760994

Typeset by The Federation Press, Leichhardt, NSW.
Printed by Ligare Pty Ltd, Riverwood, NSW

Contents

iii

Contributors

Ray Brindle is a chief Research Scientist at ARRB Transport Research Ltd in Melbourne.

Tony Dingle is Associate Professor in Economics at Monash University.

Peter Droege is Professor of Urban Design, Lend Lease Chair, Faculty of Architecture, at the University of Sydney.

Jim Falk is Professor in Science and Technology Studies, at the University of Wollongong.

Lionel Frost is Senior Lecturer in the School of Economics, Faculty of Social Sciences at La Trobe University.

Alastair Greig is Lecturer in Sociology at The Australian National University.

Don Lamberton is Visiting Fellow at the Urban Research Program, Research School of Social Sciences, at The Australian National University.

Clem Lloyd is founding Professor of Journalism at the University of Wollongong.

Jane Marceau is Professor in the Public Policy Program, at The Australian National University.

Marton Marosszeky is Associate Professor in the School of Building and Director of the Building Research Centre at the University of New South Wales.

Patrick Troy is Professor and Head of the Urban Research Program, Research School of Social Sciences, at The Australian National University.

Preface

To those who experienced the generation of neglect of the cities from 1975 the present focus on urban issues is heartening. The cycle of public concern has turned so that major questions about the nature of Australian cities are back on the national public agenda. The Commonwealth Government has invited the Industries Commission to advise it on Urban Transport, Public Housing and Taxation and Financial Policy Impacts on Urban Settlement. It has conducted the National Housing Strategy, the Review of Regional Development and the Task Force on Urban Design in Australia and it is engaged on the Australian Urban and Regional Development Review. In this focus on urban issues little attention has been paid to the history of Australian cities, how they have been shaped by their past, by economic forces and the adoption of various technologies. The disappointing aspect of this renewed interest however is that little of the debate has been research based. It has tended to take as given the present technology, especially that employed in public services.

This book is a contribution to the debate about Australian cities and how the adoption of technology in both the public and private realm creates pressures which shape them. It reports research on the impact or influence of various technologies and, while firmly eschewing the attractions of technological determinism, raises questions about the ways in which the adoption of or adherence to some technologies limits the opportunities to reshape Australian cities and indicates how adoption of particular technologies might mitigate some of the more egregious aspects of the way they operate.

The book is aimed at those in government at all three levels, at the intelligent layman and at students of the city who want to understand why our cities take the form and structure they have and how technological change affects them.

Abbreviations

ACTU	Australian Council of Trade Unions		ISDN	integrated services digital network
AI	artificial intelligence		IT	information technology
ARIP	Australian Ratings Industry Profile		JIT	just in time
			LGA	local government authority
BAS	building automation systems		MATS	Metropolitan Adelaide Transportation Study
CAD	computer aided design			
CBD	central business district		MFP	Multifunction Polis
CEO	chief executive officer		MIS	management information system
CIFM	computer integrated facilities management			
			MITI	Ministry of International Trade and Industry (Japan)
CIS	corporate information systems			
CNN	Cable News Network		MMS	maintenance management systems
CVW	corporate virtual workplaces			
			NCB	National Computer Board (Singapore)
DS	decision support			
EC	European Communities		NIMBY	not in my back yard
EDI	electronic data interchange		NTBFs	new technology-based firms
EFTPOS	electronic funds transfer point of sale		OECD	Organisation for Economic Cooperation and Development
EPOS	electronic point of sale			
ESD	ecologically sustainable development		PC	personal computer
			POLIS	power-literacy-structure
GDP	gross domestic product		PRT	personal rapid transit
GNP	gross national product		PSA	Prices Surveillance Authority
HIA	Housing Industry Association			
			QR	quick response
I&TT	information and telecommunications technology		R&D	research and development
			UPT	universal personal telecommunications
IDRC	International Development Research Centre (Canada)		VR	virtually-unaffordable-in-Reality
IS	information system		WSD	water, sewerage and drainage

Introduction

TECHNOLOGICAL CHANGE
AND URBAN DEVELOPMENT

Patrick N Troy

Technological innovations are often seen as making great changes in the way Australian cities function. It is true that the cities have indeed undergone great changes and these changes have frequently been accompanied by technological innovations, but this does not imply that technological innovations caused those changes. Technological innovations often occur in response to particular demands. How we respond socially to the innovations may then lead to effects we did not foresee, open up new opportunities for urban development or produce forces which reshape our cities. In some debates over urban issues this simple point is forgotten. This book explores technological innovations which have occurred over the recent past and the way they have affected the operation of the Australian city and how institutions of the city have responded to technological possibilities.

I   Influence of History

Cities are affected by what historians call *path dependency* (Frost & Dingle 1993). That is, decisions, practices, activities and investments made yesterday affect today's choices, which in turn affect those open to us in the future. The very site chosen when the colonies were first established, the location of the centre of command and the subdivision pattern, including access space or roads, have had a profound influence on the way each city has developed. The inherited buildings and formal spaces or the built environment, which constitutes the skeleton of a city, also influence its development and shape the options open to it even when

1

the activities carried out in the buildings differ from those for which they were originally built.

The hierarchical nature of working relations in convict settlements led to a centralised city structure. This was reinforced first by the centralised nature of transport investments and later by the water supply and sewerage networks. By the end of the 19th century Australian cities were highly centralised.

The geographic city centre was the location of the major retailing, warehousing, transport, commercial, health, education and cultural activities as well as the centre of government, law and administration.

The hierarchical nature of working relations with their short communication lines and the nature of activities carried out on a particular piece of land were often technologically constrained. The high cost and limited ability to transmit energy and information and the available materials-handling technology led to factories, warehousing, retailing and commercial developments which were very dense with little space per employee.

Factories had to be located where they could easily obtain energy — so they had to be near rail lines or wharves which delivered the coal they used in their boilers. The high cost and limited capacity to deliver energy to the work site within the factory meant that work sites were densely packed close to the site of energy generation. Warehouses were similarly intensely developed on or near rail lines and ports. The improvement in the efficiency of electricity generation and transmission and the development of efficient, reliable, small electric motors, improved hydraulic power systems, innovations in materials handling technology and more efficient road goods transport allowed more efficient, more open factories to be developed away from railways and ports.

Retail and commercial activities such as banking, finance and insurance relied on slow forms of communication and information transmission and relied heavily on manual information handling processes which in turn meant employees were densely concentrated and managed in highly hierarchical organisations. The legal system was also highly concentrated, had close communication networks and needed to be close to the centre of commerce and government. The administrative departments and agencies of government were necessarily close to the executive and to parliament.

As each city grew beyond the capacity of the locally available potable water supplies and the volume of sewage increased beyond the capacity of the local environment to absorb it, large scale, reliable supplies of water and city-wide reticulated sewerage systems were needed. Water and sewerage services were developed as highly centralised systems. Water was harvested and stored by large dams in large reservoirs and delivered under gravity by a hierarchic mains, local reservoir and reticulation network. Sewerage was the opposite. Its system involved the collection by a network of small pipes draining to larger mains which delivered the sewage to a central plant before discharge, untreated in most cases, to the ocean. The services were provided by agencies which were similarly highly centralised and hierarchical. Storm water drainage, now acknowledged as a major environmental issue, remained the responsibility of local authorities; which is one reason it has rarely been tackled as a metropolitan problem.

The provision of water supply and sewerage initially had the effect of increasing urban density. But the charging mechanisms used to finance the water and sewerage services were ultimately to give the wrong economic signals for the residential and industrial use of water. They did not discourage *leap frogging* and as a result in the early 1960s developer charges were introduced to provide some of the funds needed for servicing to encourage more efficient use of infrastructure investment and therefore more efficient development. In those areas which were developed ahead of the financial ability of the sewerage authority to provide a reticulated service the density was kept low enough to allow on site soakage of effluent from the septic systems widely used.

The health risks in 19th century Australian cities were high. To reduce the risk of illness and lessen the injury to amenity governments separated land uses. The miasmatic theory of disease transmission which was based on the hypothesis that noxious vapours spread disease, was widely accepted. Governments introduced regulations to reduce residential density in the city centre, set a minimum size for habitable rooms, separate activities within the dwelling and improve ventilation in the belief that this would reduce the incidence of disease. For similar reasons, and to reduce damage to amenity — especially for middle and upper class residents, governments introduced regulations separating malodorous and noisy land uses from residential areas. Natural lighting was required in all habitable rooms and buildings had to be spaced to allow natural light.

As the size and confidence of Australian cities developed in the second half of the 19th century there was increasing separation of civic and administrative space from *commercial* space. The increasing stress on improving the environment and notions of civic pride found expression in provision of parks, cultural facilities, monumental avenues and so on.

These works of civic pride had the effect of reducing the density of development not only of the central areas but also the emerging suburbs.

These initiatives occurred simultaneously with developing notions of what constituted *the good life* in a situation where land was much more readily available than in the European countries of origin of most migrants. In Australia the general standard of living was high which meant a higher proportion of the population could aspire to their own home on its own piece of land. This aspiration for the detached single family residence reflected and was reinforced to a significant degree by the extent of domestic production (Mullins 1981, 1988) and the need to cope with wastes on site.

The suburbanisation of the city was well under way in the mid-19th century (Davison 1993a; Frost & Dingle 1993). As the area of the city extended beyond walking distance the need for a more efficient way of providing access to the various parts of the city increased (Manning 1984).

After the First World War the notion of the garden suburb and the availability of an efficient public transport system further popularised suburban development. The increase in consumerism which followed the Second World War accelerated the suburbanisation of the city with households seeking to own their own home on its own piece of land. The popularity of the suburbs and the form of housing they contained also confirmed that households were prepared to trade off different kinds of access and housing. That is, they traded convenience to work for quality of and closeness to school — although it is also clear that they rearranged their work locations to minimise work journeys; they traded closeness to work for access to the beach and vice versa; they traded access to the city centre for closeness to the countryside and open space, and so on.

That is, the processes which led to suburbanisation of Australian cities predate all the current transport technologies with which we are familiar. Successive innovations in transport technologies have served to facilitate further spread of suburbs. These innovations, first in public transport and later via the private car, also served to give the lower income groups more equitable access to the suburbs.

II   Technological Innovation

The development of Sydney is typical of the process which occurred, with some variations, elsewhere in Australia. The demand for high-volume passenger transport was first met by the development of horse drawn buses which gradually were replaced by horse drawn trams

4

running on fixed tracks and providing a more or less regular service on radial routes to the city centre. These were followed by steam trams, cable trams and ultimately electric traction trams using the same tracks. Railways were also gradually built to meet the demand for high-volume regular services to the flourishing suburbs. These were again radial services. When motor bus services were introduced they served to feed rail services or to provide a radial service to the city centre.

Some location specific activities such as those connected with shipping were served by communities which lived close to their place of work. Although they created little demand for passenger transport these areas felt the impacts of the transport demands of the ports. Technological changes impacting on ports are not discussed in the subsequent chapters. They can, however, be used to illustrate the impact of such changes on cities. Areas like Balmain, Pyrmont and The Rocks for example provided accommodation and services for port workers and seafarers but their living areas were dissected by the rail lines and roads leading to the docks and the factories built close to them. They accommodated successive innovations in marine transport technology which affected both the ships and their portside support. Each development from small wooden hulled wind powered vessels through wrought iron to mild steel vessels powered first by wind then steam and finally diesel engines led to larger vessels with deeper draught capable of carrying larger tonnages of cargo but requiring to be *turned around* in shorter times.

These changes required changes to the portside facilities. The topography of areas such as Balmain, Pyrmont and The Rocks in Sydney, their changing relative accessibility, the fragmented pattern of property ownership and the narrow tortuous roads serving them meant that they could not easily be redeveloped to take advantage of innovations in either marine or land transport. The large *portside* areas required to assemble or unload cargoes from the new container vessels simply could not be found close to the city centres. In those rare cases where sites could be found the safety, congestion and noise problems associated with the large trucks needed to carry the containers to and from the port through the residential areas led to massive citizen opposition and the introduction of regulations which reduced the efficiency of the facilities.

The recent development of new port facilities to take advantage of marine transport innovations led to major structural changes to the metropolitan areas of most State capitals. Shipping and its support services no longer required the same or as many workers. It was no longer closely connected to the CBD. The factories the port supplied or which shipped through the port were no longer nearby — changes in plant organisation and materials handling technology had led to the suburbanisation of industrial production. Changes in the freight forwarding industry so that it became more road based and changes in warehousing facilitated by improvements in materials handling and road transport led to the suburbanisation of warehousing and factories.

It is clear that the development of air transport has had a major influence on the development of the national system of cities. The need for and development of airports has also had a major structuring effect on the individual cities. Each extension of the airports has led to major restructuring of the city.

The increase in consumerism, fed by mass advertising which developed and was supported by technological innovations such as television and new forms of credit finance, led to changes in retailing. Technological changes in retailing, its organisation, the advertising, display and sale of goods led to changes in the size of shops and their relationship to competitors.

Increased levels of car ownership allowed households to travel further to major shopping centres, to carry their weekly needs home and, using their newly acquired refrigerators, store perishable food until it was required. This led to the demise of the corner store and the competitive reorganisation and relocation of retailing, especially to the suburbs. The greater work force participation of women led to the demand for shops which were readily accessible by car in centres where most household requirements could be obtained at one stop.

Later, changes in the nature of the relationship between retailers and their suppliers was reflected in the development of *just-in-time* (JIT)and *quick response* (QR) techniques under which retailers required short supply lines and delivery times. Retailers reduced their stocks and developed highly focused marketing strategies which relied on the ability of manufacturers and wholesalers to supply them at short notice. The involvement of retailers in quality control also required closer relations between manufacturers and retailers thus affecting the location of shops and the factories which supply them. Changes in the way retailers related to their suppliers and to their customers thus led to changes in the demand for transport and information services.

The recent changes in retailing in which the boundaries between retailing and wholesaling are being blurred, together with the advent of 24 hour shopping will lead to a new round of changes in the trip generation pattern of retail services.

Developments in structural engineering and elevators allowed the construction of yet taller buildings. Individuals and corporations competed to build the tallest as monuments to their power and command over technology and permitting larger numbers of workers to be accommodated in the city centre.

Innovations in office management have also affected land use in the sense that office workers now take up less floor space than they did formerly. The intensification of office development in the central city which has occurred over the past three decades means that central city offices can accommodate more people which in turn means that although the central city work force has not grown substantially the transport system is required to have the capacity to deliver more people to a location within the central area in a given time than it did. Recent oversupply of office space has given firms the opportunity to relocate more easily within the central city which in turn has meant greater variability in the location of the peak demand within the central area.

Major innovations in information technology have been used to facilitate changes in the organisation and operation of firms and government agencies. The widespread use of telecommunications systems (fixed and mobile telephones, fax, electronic mail and data transmission), word processors, micro computers, electronic data storage, laser printers, photocopiers and better software has led to office reorganisation which has reduced office space per person. This has occurred because employees have been grouped closer together to share equipment and because the standardisation of correspondence and routinisation of office functions has meant that more employees do their own typing and record keeping. At least as important, though, is the way this technology has reduced the need for employees to be in a central location — or even at a fixed location. The developments in information technology have allowed firms to locate their *back office* functions outside central cities; in suburban areas or in other cities. But the same technologies have also allowed employees and service workers who need to have close contact with clients to spend most, if not all, their time *on the road*, transmitting orders from telephones, faxes and computers in their cars. And of course these technologies allow some to work from their homes.

Changes in labour deployment in the form of multi-skilling and management practices in the form of flatter organisational structures together with changes in the relations between manufacturers and their suppliers and clients led to significant changes in the use of people and their movement to and from factories. That is, a given factory now uses fewer employees under more flexible hours which means fewer peak hour work journeys but the greater product variation and shorter ordering cycles means more frequent supplier deliveries and client service trips.

The private car was developed to meet demands for independence, security, safety, speed, comfort and privacy. Over the past 40 years a variety of technological innovations have made cars more secure, safer, more comfortable, more private, offering greater independence, more affordable, more reliable, easier to drive, faster, and less polluting per kilometre travelled. In other words, the car has come closer to meeting very strongly held desires of the population. Many of the innovations in cars also make it easier for businesses to pursue their activities.

Developments in structural engineering, soil mechanics, pavement design and control systems have made the road system safer and cheaper to construct and operate.

Fixed track public transport also has experienced significant innovations in the safety, cleanliness, comfort and economy of the vehicles and in the safety and economy of the permanent way. Improvements in control systems have made the system safer and more reliable. The inability of public transport to offer independence or flexibility and privacy, however, has meant that in relative terms it has fallen in popularity. The radial pattern of the fixed track public transport services has meant that they have not been able to adapt to the changes in the pattern of demand arising from the suburbanisation of employment and social and cultural activities. As a result there has been little investment in the systems which has led to further reduction in patronage.

Although this brief Introduction makes clear some of the major effects of the adoption of technological innovation on the Australian city it should be acknowledged that they have not been costless. Some of the changes have been attended by significant dislocation and others by environmental externalities which the cities are only now beginning to address.

III   About This Book

This book is in three parts. In Part I the book explores a number of changes in technology from a historical perspective. Part II discusses technological changes in particular services or aspects of the city and their impact on city form and structure. Part III explores the impact of cities as a whole on the process of innovation.

Part I Historical Perspective

Frost and Dingle provide a more detailed historical perspective on the impact of technological change. They show that cities have been producers of technology and that their growth has been influenced by it. They make the point that Australian cities have always been *up with the latest* and in some cases have adopted new technologies at an astounding rate. They open up the issue of the way the public and private spheres adopted new technology indicating ways in which the responses of the two spheres influenced the city.

Part II Technological Change and Urban Services

One of the earliest and most enduring influences on the city is the investment in transport services. Ray Brindle points out that transport and land use are intimately connected and that the demands originating from the way we organise and use urban space has shaped and been shaped by the transport investments we have made. He warns against physical determinism and the current fashion for increasing urban density as a way of solving urban problems including transportation. Brindle argues that the accessibility of a city is modified by the level of mobility of its residents and that attempts to reshape the city to reduce travel demand are doomed, whatever other effect they might have.

In discussing water, sewerage and drainage, Clem Lloyd argues that while urban development is dependent on the availability of a sustainable supply of potable water, it has been unresponsive to technological changes in the water supply/sewerage/drainage industry. The form of development has been affected by the technology employed in providing sewerage and drainage services and new approaches to the pricing of water supply sewerage and drainage might lead to technological innovations which will have even greater impact on future urban form.

We have heard much of late about the information highway and the significance of technological developments in this field to the way we live, work and seek our cultural stimulations. In short we are advised that our cities will undergo major changes as a consequence. Don Lamberton's chapter draws our attention to the impact of past developments in our capacity to communicate but suggests that any causal connection between improved communication and economic growth remains problematic. He argues that the form and structure of the cities, at least in the developed economies, is shaped by the availability of communication services and by the flows of information and that while innovations in information technology will continue to influence the cities, their influences will not be without cost.

In his discussion of retailing Alastair Greig points out that postmodern theorists argue that consumption patterns are the crucial determinants of identity formation and that retailing and shopping malls have assumed greater importance as *cathedrals of consumption*. He also suggests that more conventional economic theorists should acknowledge the importance of retailing in product and process innovation. Greig outlines the changes which have occurred in retailing in Australia over the recent past and suggests that this has had a major restructuring effect on the city. He discusses the impact of innovations in information technology on the operation of the industry and implies that the involvement of retailing in quality control may lead to another round of industrial development in the city because of the need for closer connections between manufacturing and retailing.

In the past the form of urban development was significantly affected by our understanding of how materials behaved and by the stage of development of construction materials. In his chapter Marton Marosszeky points out that technological constraints on the size of buildings are now insignificant. Advances in our capacity to analyse and design buildings and in the three major construction materials (steel, concrete and glass) mean we can now build virtually any kind of building of any scale anywhere we want — the constraints are now more likely to be social, economic and aesthetic.

Part III The City and Innovation

Jane Marceau explores the ways in which innovation and technological change have influenced the manufacturing process and thus the structure of firms. She argues that these changes have not of themselves had substantial impacts on the form and structure of the city — it all depends on how the firms decide to put the new technological possibilities into practice. Marceau offers three approaches to the analysis of innovation, each of which reveals only a partial picture of the situation and has different implications for the spatial arrangement of manufacturing.

Jim Falk discusses the notion of cities as generators of technological innovation. He argues that although cities are where the market is and where most of the productive activity takes place they have rarely been conceived or structured as either effective communities or politically significant actors. Falk suggests that it is possible to see the world as a *set* of competing city regions and that there would be virtue in paying more attention to the role of cities in innovation. He argues, for example, that innovation in the way we tackle environmental issues may be achieved best at the city level suggesting that we would need to strengthen our notion of community and exploit the differences between our cities to do so.

The final chapter by Peter Droege presents a glimpse into the future and provides a broad look at technology, institutional policy and design in the information age. Droege argues that cities have always been organised around the management of information but that we now have a vastly enhanced capacity to exchange information. This must inevitably express itself in the way we organise and use the urban space in which we live.

IV   Social Change and Technological Innovation

As living standards have risen people have had greater choice in their domestic lives in a variety of ways. One of the main choices they have made has been to consume more urban space, to make themselves more comfortable.

This has been partly in the form of larger, better equipped dwellings and control over private open space — that is, gardens. (We should note a paradox that over the post-war period the size of urban lots, and therefore gardens, has actually fallen significantly meaning that net residential density in newly developed areas has risen in the order of 100 per cent. This may be a result of increasing scarcity and hence cost of space as cities have grown.)

Another choice has been to spend more time on leisure and other non-work activities. A very high proportion of this increased private time has been spent in home-based activities including gardening. As increased proportions of people take early retirement, both voluntary and involuntary, we can expect them to spend even more time in and around the homes, and to want private urban space in which to spend that time.

They have also increased their demand for urban public space. That is, they have wanted more public space for their passive and active recreations and for their cultural and social activities. We see this in the increase in provision of golf courses and a wide variety of sports grounds but also in the demand for *promenade* space and centres such as "Darling Harbour" in Sydney.

Family size has fallen, people marry later, have fewer children and more women remain in the work force. These social changes have occurred at the same time as a shorter working week. These changes

11

tend to change the demand for transport services. For example, now that two members of many households work, minimisation of the journey to work in length or time will frequently produce a different result from the period when only one worked — typically in a central city location.

Given choices about where to work and live, where to locate their businesses, and where to shop and pass their leisure time, people have chosen dispersed locations and they use the shopping, recreational and cultural facilities at different times. They seek convenience, comfort, privacy, security and economy in the ways they obtain access to those destinations. Moreover, they want to have that access as quickly as possible when and in whatever sequence they choose.

In many Australian cities, especially the larger of them, there is now more than one centre. That is the changes wrought by the adoption of a variety of technological innovations and social changes has meant that the traditional centre is no longer the dominant centre for retailing, warehousing, transport, commerce, health, education or cultural activities. The traditional centre remains the focus of political, administrative and financial power but this *off-centred* location of power is the cause of much of the stress under which our cities operate. The attempt to retain the historic centre as the dominant centre of the city results in additional travel and leads to distortion in transport investment.

The net effect of these restructuring forces resulting from technological change and changing social behaviour is that we are seeing major changes in the nature of relationships between transport and land use. The proportion of all work trips which are to or from the city centre has fallen to less than 20 per cent, and about 35 per cent of work trips are to jobs within the same local government area in which the worker lives. Apart from the trips to the city centre, the average length of work trip has fallen. But more importantly work trips are now about 30 per cent of all trips, although they account for about 35 per cent of distance travelled. An even higher proportion of non-work trips are for activities which are not centrally located. In terms of total travel, the journey to work is now less important than, say, recreational travel.

The Australian city, then, has been subjected to a variety of dynamic processes which have affected and been affected by social changes, technological innovation and changing choice among the private and public activities and endeavours of individuals and enterprises.

Recognition of the dynamic nature of land uses and their relationship with one another and the demand for infrastructure services should lead us to conclude that we cannot rely on physical determinist notions of static relationships. We should try to use the inherent dynamism in each city in planning for and providing these infrastructure services.

The current preoccupation with consolidation policies stems from a notion of fixed relationships between transport and land uses. It assumes people can be organised and constrained to support the city centre and to make it economical to operate a fixed rail transit system. The approach seems to assume that we come together in cities to justify the operation of a fixed rail transit system rather than for our social or economic well being. There seems little logic other than to serve the interests of transit operators, the owners of central city offices and possibly some developers, in trying to constrain people's choice in where and how they should live to make the provision of a fixed rail system economically feasible.

In recognising the inherent dynamism of the urban system we should recognise that people can make choices and judgments and that the history of Australian urbanisation, especially the recent history, suggests that they are well aware of the consequences of their decisions. But the urban system should not inhibit or prevent the city from accommodating itself to new technology or changes in social relations or economic processes.

The strategy we should adopt in planning our cities should be based on recognition that we will continue to adopt technological innovations, that behaviour will continue to change, that relationships between land uses will continue to be dynamic and that there is therefore a need for greater flexibility in planning for infrastructure services. Transport planning, for example, should be directed at keeping options open. This approach would lead to less emphasis on providing infrastructure to service the present city centre and more, on equity grounds, on the provision of services to metropolitan centres of industry, commerce and culture. It should recognise that we no longer have a single-centred city and that social desires and technological innovations are unlikely to lead to a return to that structure of our urban areas.

Good point – need to decide what the priorities are first.

13

Chapter 1

INFRASTRUCTURE, TECHNOLOGY AND CHANGE: A historical perspective[1]

Lionel Frost and Tony Dingle

Technological change is the means by which societies can increase efficiency and reduce waste in the productive process and so expand their potential for economic growth. As Joel Mokyr notes, technological creativity: "has been one of the most potent forces in history in that it has provided society with ... an increase in output that is not commensurate with the increase in effort and cost necessary to bring it about". It is the essence of economic growth, bringing about "rising living standards, ... improving nutrition, clothing, housing, and health, and ... reducing toil, drudgery, famine, and disease" (Mokyr 1990: 3).

The development of Australia by white settlers took place in a particular technological context. In the century preceding the First World War, European nation states made use of new technology to conquer Africa and much of Asia and colonise land in the Americas and Australasia. This new technology involved the application of steam power and iron to ships, riverboats, and railroads; new communications technology, notably the submarine cable, which was invaluable for diplomacy and business transactions and information; improved firearms, which helped to suppress the indigenous population; and new medicines which reduced the impact of tropical disease on Europeans

1   We are grateful to the School of Economics and Commerce, LaTrobe University, for a School Research Grant and to the Faculty of Business and Economics, Monash University, for finance which made possible the collection of part of the material used in this chapter. Judy Francis and Seamus O'Hanlon provided excellent research assistance.

(Headrick 1981). As European industrialisation created increased demand for food and raw materials, the transfer of European technology and institutions turned the colonies into supply regions. A world economy developed, based on the exchange of European capital, labour and industrial goods for colonial resources.

Cities played a crucial role as producers and consumers within this world economy. Colonial port cities were their regions' link with European markets and imports. These and other smaller towns acted as bases for the opening up of new land, providing farmers, ranchers, and miners with goods and services which were essential to commercial production. They also provided transport links to the port cities. Cities and towns were also the location of the various levels of government, which provided infrastructure and a framework of law and order.

It has been argued that the transfer of technology from Europe to its colonies in the tropics widened the economic gap between the two regions (Headrick 1988). The colonial economies remained simple and underdeveloped, and vulnerable to shifts in world demand for the primary products they supplied. On the other hand, Australia's record of economic growth stands out clearly as an example of successful adaptation of European methods of farming and manufacturing to a new environment and different factor proportions (White 1992). There was a "creative response" to problems posed by poor soils, natural shocks, limited markets, and high labour costs. This involved the rapid diffusion and adaptation of overseas technologies and in some cases the invention of new ones. This chapter explores two issues: first, to what extent was this technological change stimulated by the growth of Australian cities? Second, how was new technology used to cope with the problems which resulted from urban growth and how did the rate at which new technology was adopted vary between cities?

I   Cities as Producers of New Technology

Fernand Braudel once wrote that "Towns are like electric transformers" (Braudel 1981: 479). For Braudel, the characteristic feature of a town is that it contributes to economic development by providing services and markets and a location within a network of transport and communication which encourages people in the surrounding countryside to become market-minded, specialist producers. As towns prospered and grew larger there was an incentive for their inhabitants to improve business practices and facilities for trade.

This theme has been taken up by Jane Jacobs (1985). For Jacobs, economic growth takes place when people in cities are able to replace imported goods with those made locally, and then in turn exporting these goods to other markets. This import replacement transforms the economy of the surrounding region by creating new markets for food and raw materials thereby encouraging technological change in agriculture, new urban jobs which may be filled by surplus land workers, transplants of urban work to lower-cost, non-urban locations (such as the development of protoindustry), and by the generation of urban capital which is invested in the region's infrastructure. The creation of new work is most likely to originate from cities because they contain specialist producers who can provide innovators with skilled labour, spare parts and other inputs.

Cities are therefore places which create economic growth by producing new technology, rather than simply consuming the technology which is made available by economic growth originating from other sources. These writers are making a case for a specifically urban contribution to economic development, with urbanisation being an independent variable in the process of technological change and economic growth.

These arguments are persuasive but difficult to test. While the major periods of economic growth in world history have been characterised by urbanisation, it is difficult to say with precision whether city growth is a cause of economic growth or an effect of it.

The first Australian settlements were established when the Industrial Revolution was in full swing. Penal settlements had a substantial urban population of convicts, soldiers, and administrators at the outset. The development of the wool industry from the 1820s created urban work in the provision of processing, storage, handling, financial, and other commercial services. By 1830, 30 per cent of the Australian population lived in towns with at least 2500 inhabitants, compared to only nine per cent in the United States (Frost 1990: 17). The Gold Rushes and the expansion of agricultural production created new towns and accelerated the growth of established ones. Australia remained significantly more urbanised than the United States, Canada, Argentina, or New Zealand throughout the 19th century.

This rapid urban growth called for heavy investment in city-building. During the second half of the 19th century, house building became the leading field of investment, accounting for more than one-third of total capital formation (Butlin 1964: 11). When housing shortages developed, such as after the Gold Rushes, or seemed likely to develop as individual cities started to grow rapidly, the construction sector responded and the quality of the housing stock was at least maintained, and usually improved (Frost 1991: 104-7).

This reflected, in part, high levels of average per capita incomes, and therefore effective demand for housing, and the ability and willingness of colonial governments to use overseas borrowings to pay for the infrastructure needed for suburban development. But the physical quality of Australian townscapes also reflected the quick diffusion of overseas building technology which saved labour and reduced construction costs. Foremost was an "architectural revolution" in house construction (Cronon 1991: 179), known as the "balloon-frame" method, which involved the joining of light timber studs, joists, and rafters by nailing. This made building quicker, easier, and cheaper than previous methods, in which heavy timbers were joined by mortice and tenoning. The technique speeded up construction by reducing the need for skilled and unskilled labour, especially in the suburbs, where lower population densities reduced the fire risk of timber construction (Frost & Jones 1989). The balloon-frame was developed by builders in Chicago shortly after that city's foundation in 1830. It was the balloon-frame method and the abundance of cheap lumber which enabled Chicago's housing stock to roughly keep pace with population growth, as the city's population rocketed from 100,000 in 1860 to one million in 1890, and to two million in 1910 (Frost 1991: 104). In Chicago and in other United States cities, unskilled immigrants could buy a book of house plans and build their own houses with the help of neighbours and friends (Harris 1988).

It is clear that Australians were building wooden houses this way by the time of the Gold Rushes, but it is unclear whether it was migrants from North America who brought the technology with them, or whether Australians learnt of the method through written reports or some other source. King (1984) suggests that early Australian housing may have been influenced strongly by the preferences of British military personnel who had previously served in hot colonies such as India, where houses were built with large verandahs. But the process by which balloon-frame technology spread to various regions is shadowy: it is by no means inconceivable that here Australians "re-invented the wheel" by developing simple construction techniques without knowledge of similar developments in regions elsewhere. To our knowledge, the term "balloon-frame" itself has never used in Australia.

Regardless of its origin, the balloon frame method spread to the suburbs of Australian cities, and to those of Canada and New Zealand as well. Adelaide was the main exception because there cheap local stone provided the basic building material. In compact 19th century Sydney brick terrace houses predominated, but in Melbourne most houses were cottages built of wood (McCarty 1970: 83). The basic features of the balloon-frame – simple, light weatherboard construction

– were in the 20th century embodied in the California Bungalow, which was very popular in United States, Canadian, and Australian cities. Kenneth Jackson, who writes that the "new method of building was as unique to the United States as the idea of low density suburbs itself" (Jackson 1985: 128), understates both the extent to which this technology was used in other countries, and the general preference of city-dwellers in Anglo-Celtic societies for suburban living.

There were other advances in building technology and practice which simplified construction and thus saved labour. In general, these were overseas inventions which were adopted quickly in Australia. They included the use of machine woodworking tools, prefabrication of doors and windows, and the use of bricks which were machine-made and therefore of uniform size and easier to lay. Galvanised iron, imported from England, provided cheap material for roofing. Cavity brick walls, which from the 1890s allowed houses to be built with two layers of bricks instead of three, were an Australian invention (Pikusa 1986: 63). In the 20th century the principle was taken a step further with the development of brick-veneer houses, with a single layer of brick tied to a balloon-frame.

Most house building was done by small-scale builders who were usually short of capital and obtained land and building materials on credit. As in the United States, the system of subcontracting work to specialist plumbers and gasfitters, bricklayers, plasterers and other tradesmen reduced construction time and costs (Doucet & Weaver 1985). Builders did the simple frame construction which required little skill or experience. The result of cost-cutting was often shoddy workmanship, so that by the First World War many of the houses which had been built during the 1870s and 1880s were described as slums fit only for demolition. Nevertheless, in a competitive market builders passed on savings to buyers. As incomes rose building costs remained stable and people opted for roomier rather than cheaper houses. Over time the average house and lot size increased, which meant that more suburban railways and tramways, sewers, water pipes and other infrastructure would be needed. Furthermore, some manufacturers enjoyed larger markets as people stuffed their houses with furniture and household goods.

In Australian cities there were changes made to business practices and institutions in an attempt to "capture" the benefits of innovation. For instance, the development of a banking system played a crucial role in raising finance for the expansion of the wool industry during the first half of the 19th century (see Butlin 1953). A few large metropolitan-based banks were able to serve pastoralists and farmers conveniently by establishing a system of branches in small towns. As the development of the steamship and the telegraph speeded up the transfer of goods and information, foreign manufacturers were able to increase their share of the value of the export trade by establishing their own agents in overseas markets, rather than continuing to do business with local merchants. The effects of foreign competition brought about significant changes in commercial practice in Melbourne during the 1880s. A new Commercial Exchange was opened in 1880 and this and a growing number of trade journals provided improved information and means of communication. Shorthand writers, typewriters and new methods of bookkeeping were introduced (Davison 1978: 19-29). City life became more ordered and efficient with the introduction of standardised time to integrate railway timetables, postal services and other urban activities (Davison 1993).

During the 19th century Australian manufacturing was stimulated by urbanisation. At first, processing and manufacturing of rural output and inputs was done using simple techniques in small-scale enterprises close to farms. Thus as the South Australian wheat frontier expanded during the 1870s, flour mills and agricultural implement factories could be found in most rural towns, even those with only around a hundred inhabitants (Meinig 1962: 197-201). But as railway and telegraph networks enabled metropolitan merchants and manufacturers to obtain raw materials from, and dispatch goods to, country areas, the days of small town producers were numbered. Metropolitan firms could take advantage of economies of scale and agglomeration to invest in new technology. The cheap plains to the west of Melbourne were aesthetically drab, but offered advantages to manufacturers such as HV McKay, who moved his "Sunshine" harvester factory there from Ballarat in 1904 (Lack 1986). Flour milling technology became more efficient with the importation of roller milling equipment. Brewing was transformed in 1888 by the development of a pure yeast culture suited to Australian conditions by a Belgian brewer working in Melbourne, and by the arrival in Melbourne of the Foster brothers from New York, who brought lager brewing equipment with them (Fellows of the Australian Academy of Technological Sciences and Engineering 1988: 72-6, 104-6). Metropolitan butter factories adopted new technology, notably the cream separator and the Babcock tester of butter fat content, on a large scale, which enabled them to force most small town factories out of business (Frost 1991: 50-1). The economic advantages of metropolitan location allowed manufacturers to at least partially offset the limitations of shortages of capital, high labour costs, and a small domestic market.

The issue of whether it is slow population growth and shortages of labour which stimulate labour-saving technological change is a complex one. Simon (1986) has argued that on the one hand, rapid population growth will increase the level of aggregate demand and therefore stimulate innovation, but at the same time the extra labour supply may depress wage levels and discourage innovation. The net effect of population increase on technological change is therefore indeterminate, rather than negative as is conventionally assumed. On the other hand, slower population growth, which was characteristic of Australia, increased wage levels, which may be expected to have stimulated innovation. Witness, for instance, the high standard of finish and equipment in Australian houses (Kelly 1978; Young 1992). Nevertheless, the small domestic market placed manufacturers at a disadvantage, unless they could locate in metropolitan areas to take advantage of economies of scale, agglomeration, and large transport and distribution networks.

Many new technologies came from overseas: roller milling equipment came from Hungary in 1879; the cream separator was invented in Sweden in 1878 and the Babcock tester in the USA in 1890. However, many notable technological advances were made by migrants *after* they arrived in Australia. A Scot developed the world's first ice-making machinery at Geelong in 1851. A Lancastrian working in Sydney used this technique to develop refrigerated shipping which was used to land Australian (and Argentine) meat, butter, and other perishable produce in Europe (Farrer 1980: 183-200). Migrants working in Melbourne, Sydney, and Grafton, New South Wales, made important advances in canning technology (Farrer 1980: 65-93; Fellows of the Australian Academy of the Technological Sciences and Engineering 1988: 77-88). Farmers from diverse ethnic backgrounds made important advances in clearing, ploughing, irrigating, sowing, fertilising, and harvesting. This was made possible by adapting and modifying existing implements, as was the case with the stump-jump plough or by inventing new ones, such as the mallee roller, which simply involved the dragging of a large log or old iron boiler over mallee scrub to break it down before burning. During the 1890s, farmers on South Australia's Yorke Peninsula experimented with the use of seed drills to apply superphosphate to worn out land. At Minlaton, John Cudmore adapted techniques of drilling and manuring which he had learned on a farm in his native Devon (*South Yorke's Peninsula Pioneer* 1900). Joseph Correll and his brothers Edward and William, who conducted further drilling experiments, were originally from Ireland.[2] A large number of farmers throughout the Australian wheat belt selected strains of early-maturing wheat which resisted drought and rust. Complementing the inventiveness of farmers was the work of government agricultural experts. The wheat breeding of William Farrer is well known, but there were several unsung heroes: for instance, in Victoria's Department of Agriculture Alfred Pearson compiled important information on the chemistry of Australian soils, while the indefatigable plant pathologist Daniel McAlpine wrote several books and scores of papers on fungus diseases of plants and crops. Pearson was raised on a farm in Yorkshire and McAlpine was born in Ayrshire, Scotland (Frost 1982: 121-30).

It may be argued that while farmers were themselves practical and inventive and agricultural experts talented and hard working, it was above all the stimulus of urban markets, both in Australia and overseas, which brought about this technological change. The level of rural prosperity was an important influence on the growth of government revenue and urban jobs, and so policies to increase farm production and productivity were generally supported by the urban as well as rural electorate (Frost 1992). By the end of the 1860s, when the Australian colonies had introduced legislation to make Crown land available for individual family farms:

> [T]he ideal of a self-supporting yeomanry was gone and in its place there had emerged the reality of a foot-loose population engaged in a business-like approach to agriculture, specialising in wheat growing for a world-wide competitive market. (Williams 1974: 37)

Most farmers were at first cautious about changing their methods, but once the effectiveness of new technologies could be demonstrated change came rapidly. Saving labour and reducing production costs was important if farming was to be commercially successful. Farmers were constantly on the lookout for ways to produce good crops in dry seasons, while keeping production costs down to minimise losses if a drought occurred. Once farmers could with confidence send perishable produce to overseas markets, the scale of dairying and meat export activities increased. Where railways provided easy access to the major cities, farmers diversified their operations and increased production of meat, dairy produce, hay, fruit and vegetables.

By responding to growing urban markets, farming became more efficient and the average farm became capable of serving a larger urban population: between 1861 and 1891 Melbourne's population grew by 278 per cent, while the number of farmers rose by only 188 per cent; the

---

2   We are indebted to Mr Brenton Correll for this information.

average number of Melbourne residents served by every 100 farmers increased from 357 to 446 — an increase in productivity of 25 per cent, or 0.8 per cent per annum (Census of Victoria, 1861, 1891). This supports Wrigley's (1985) argument about the urban contribution to the growth of agricultural productivity in England from 1650 to 1750, and suggests a strong causal role played by urbanisation in the process of technological change. Australian cities therefore helped to produce new technology as well as consume it.

II Technology and City Growth

To function effectively, cities need to provide workable and affordable housing, sanitation, energy, communications, and journey-to-work arrangements. Cities which are favoured by high average incomes and governments with the will and tax base to tackle urban problems are best able to meet these costs. In weaker city economies with large numbers of low-income inhabitants and ineffective government, the costs of building, equipping, and servicing the city have to be kept to a minimum. Existing houses may be subdivided or modified, or people may be allowed to build their own shelter on unwanted land. This will create cheap housing for a growing low-income population, but may lead to increased risk of epidemics or fire. Because the market cannot put a price on fresh air, clean water, and road space, individuals may use these scarce resources in a way which reduces the supply and quality available to others, thus creating externalities. Unless government provides adequate infrastructure and a correct pricing policy to tax or penalise those who overuse resources, the economic and environment costs of city living will mount up (Frost 1993). It has been argued that such endogenous increases in costs act as limits to city size by cutting disposable incomes and capital accumulation (Kelley & Williamson 1984). But if governments get their policies right, big cities can be sustained and society's capacity for technological change will be enhanced.

During the early stages of their development Australian cities, like their United States counterparts, were rough and raw places. The technology used to cope with urban problems was labour-intensive, primitive, inefficient, and in some cases dangerous: potable water was delivered by private water carriers; muddy streets restricted movement; streets, waterways, and wells were polluted by sewage and refuse; the risk of fire in districts built cheaply of impermanent materials was high. At the height of the Gold Rush a reporter contended:

[T]hat a worse regulated, worse governed, worse drained, worse lighted, worse watered town of note is not on the face of the globe; . . . in a word, nowhere in the southern hemisphere does chaos reign so triumphant as in Melbourne (quoted by Frost 1991: 118).

During the 19th century all the major Australian cities had to cope with bursts of population growth. Between 1881 and 1891 both Sydney and Melbourne grew at almost six per cent per annum. Adelaide's population rose by almost nine per cent per annum between 1876 and 1881. After a long period of sluggish growth Brisbane and Perth grew very quickly at the end of the century: Brisbane by almost 12 per cent per annum from 1881 to 1891, and Perth by 14 per cent per annum from 1891 to 1901 and by almost six per cent per annum during the following decade (McCarty 1970). Such episodes put great strains on existing infrastructure and externalities mounted.

The aptly named "network" technologies introduced into the growing cities of Europe and the United States from the mid-19th century sought to overcome the externalities generated by urban growth and so allow continued urbanisation. Reticulated water supplies and underground water-borne sewerage systems helped reduce death rates from infectious diseases and clean up the urban environment. Gas and electricity distribution systems made public places lighter and safer, lit homes and factories and provided the growing energy inputs for urban living and production. Suburban roads, trains and railways pushed out suburban boundaries, enlarging the metropolitan living area. Telegraph and telephone provided the more powerful means of communication necessary to keep the expanding urban system working effectively.

Initially new technology flowed from Europe to America, but towards the end of the century, the United States became the main innovator and the flow was reversed. The rate of change picked up as massive investments saw the major cities in the United States and Europe "progressing to the stage where they were fully networked with wires, pipes, and tracks" by the eve of the First World War (Tarr & Dupuy, 1988: xiv-xv). So far urban historians in Australia have paid relatively little attention to the rate of technical change in the cities or to the factors influencing the speed with which these network technologies were adopted. There have been some excellent monographs of particular networks but no comparative studies of the same technology in the major Australian cities, despite the fact that Australia's capital cities in particular provide an ideal framework for comparative studies.

Information about new developments reached Australia relatively rapidly, so lack of knowledge never seems to have delayed the introduction of new technology significantly. Local branches of professional bodies, especially of engineers, kept their members up to date through meetings and through their journals. The international labour market for engineers meant that foreign trained and experienced engineers brought knowledge with them when they took up the many local positions which opened up as the necessary infrastructures needed by a growing economy were built. The colonial tradition of calling in an overseas expert — usually British — also helped to keep Australia up with best practices. So too did the major international exhibitions which featured new scientific and engineering advances; the Centennial Exhibition in Melbourne in 1888 featured a large electricity generating plant (Cannon 1975: 98).

Some network technologies were transferred with great rapidity. Electricity was a novelty source of light for several decades. Before it could become a network technology it was necessary to develop a more reliable source of light than the arc lamp, a method of transferring electricity long distances from its point of generation and the development of large capacity generators which could produce cheap electricity. All these breakthroughs were made in either Germany or the United States during the 1880s (Derry & Williams 1960: ch 22). Within a decade parts of most of Australia's cities had electric street lighting. Tamworth, Young, Penrith, Mossvale and Newcastle had it before Sydney, so mere size of town does not appear to have influenced the speed with which electricity was introduced. Launceston had 30 miles of street lighting by 1896 while in Hobart and Brisbane, well entrenched gas companies delayed the introduction of electric street lighting until the 20th century (Cannon 1975: 108-116). The Redfern generating station, which opened in 1890, was the first to supply an extended area with electricity but a similar plant was opened in Burnley in Melbourne a year later and the big generating station in Spencer Street, which is still in use, began operating in 1894.

Telephones were also adopted rapidly. Alexander Graham Bell patented a practical telephone in 1876. Two years later Britain's first telephone company was set up. Henry Byron Moore's Melbourne Telephone Exchange Company began operating in August 1880 with a 100 line switchboard. Sydney opened its first exchange in the same month, Brisbane did so within a year, while Adelaide and Hobart began in 1883. From 1891 one of the world's first call-girl networks was operating in Melbourne as the city's leading brothels installed telephones (Cannon 1975: 120-121).

By 1901 there were over 6000 telephone lines in Victoria, most of them in Melbourne. Within 20 years there had been an eight fold increase (Victorian Yearbook, 1993). Throughout the Commonwealth as a whole, a quarter of a million phones were in use by 1920 (less than 5000 of them were public phones). This worked out at just over four phones for every hundred people. Phones attached to central city exchanges — which would have been largely business phones — made an average of over eight outward calls each day. Phones linked to suburban exchanges averaged four outward calls a day, but those in country areas only two. By 1938 over 630,000 phones were connected (10,500 of them were public phones), which gave a ratio of nine phones to every hundred people. Interestingly the intensity of use appears not to have changed significantly. Central city daily calls had increased slightly to ten but suburban and country users had not changed (Commonwealth Yearbooks).

The invisible network of radio waves, the aptly named wireless, spread even more rapidly. Despite a licence fee amounting to about a fifth of the average weekly wage, the cost of a receiver, and a major depression, the number of listeners' licences increased tenfold in the decade after 1925 and had exceeded one million by 1938. This was a ratio of 15 licences for every 100 people, a level exceeded only by the United States at 20, Denmark at 18, Britain, Sweden and New Zealand (Commonwealth Yearbooks).

The response of the cities to the challenge of providing public transport was far more varied, both in respect to the technology they chose and the speed with which it was introduced. The siting and planning of Australian cities has had an important influence on the type of infrastructure technology needed to cope with the problems of urban growth. Sydney and Brisbane began as penal settlements and were not expected to support large populations. Sydney was founded at a constricted site and its street system was basically unplanned. The New South Wales Parliament was dominated by a "country interest" which regarded Sydney as a vast parasite and only invested in urban improvement grudgingly. Public transport remained a perennial problem throughout the 19th century, as there was no suitable open space for a convenient railway terminus and hilly streets were not suited to horse trams. In the absence of any link between the rail terminus at Redfern and the major workplaces at Sydney Cove (a tramway providing this service opened in 1861 but closed five years later), railways were largely ineffective for commuting. In 1879 the colonial government introduced steam trams in an attempt to solve the public transport problem cheaply. These proved highly unpopular: they were noisy, slow, and covered passengers and nearby houses with soot and smoke (Fitzgerald 1987: 58-9). In some districts, such as Paddington, privately operated horse-drawn omnibuses provided reasonably efficient service for commuters (Audley 1983). But for most people the best solution was to live close to where they worked, in compact terrace housing. By 1891, 86 per cent of Sydney's population lived within walking distance — around two miles — of Sydney Cove (Frost 1991: 26).

Brisbane needed to have bridges built to expand beyond its small site which was hemmed in on three sides by the Brisbane River. Trams began operating in 1885, but only one bridge provided access to land across the River and by the end of the decade suburban developers "were running into difficulties" (Davison 1987: 224).

Melbourne, Adelaide, and Perth were founded as commercial cities. Their respective colonial parliaments were dominated by members who represented or lived in the capital. Railways were needed to link the town centres with distant port towns (Williamstown, Port Melbourne, Port Adelaide, and Fremantle). This early railway development exerted an abiding influence on the cities' public transport and spatial structure. By the start of the 1880s the centre of Melbourne was served by three rail termini (two had been built by private companies and then taken over by the State) and it was extension of the railway network which played the key role in opening up new areas with suburban potential. The location of the main Adelaide rail terminus in the northern parklands meant that railway lines ran around the western edge of the city. As a result, the eastern suburbs never had a railway and commuters walked or took a tram to work. Trams were more convenient for commuters in the southern suburbs, especially those who worked in the southern part of the city centre. Adelaide's wide streets and generally flat topography were well suited to horse trams and these were introduced, as in Melbourne, in the 1870s. In Perth, the railway to Fremantle provided the key corridor of suburban expansion, creating a linear region of suburbs north of the Swan River. This line has been recently re-opened, electrified and re-equipped, its success confounding those who see public transport cutbacks as the only workable solution to urban transport problems (see Newman 1992a).

Efficient public transport was an important precondition for the low density development which was characteristic of Melbourne, Adelaide, and Perth. These "New Frontier" cities, like their counterparts in the American West, were highly suburbanised and covered far more ground than congested cities like Sydney and those of eastern North America. By spreading outwards to cope with population growth, the New Frontier cities avoided many of the problems associated with high density living (Frost 1991). However dispersed living did raise the cost of the provision of network technologies to every household. This was especially the case in Melbourne during the boom years of the 1880s when tramways and suburban railways engaged in cutthroat competition for customers. This resulted in the construction of a suburban tram and train network with a massive over-capacity which would take another generation to absorb (Davison 1970). The capital invested could have been used more productively elsewhere and NG Butlin has argued that this was part of a growing structural imbalance in the Australian economy which helped precipitate the depression of the 1890s (Butlin 1964: ch 6).

The timing of the introduction of transport technologies was often determined as much by squabbles between interested parties as by the availability of particular technologies. Once decisions were made however they could influence future choices. This carry-over effect from one historical period to the next is what economic historians call path dependency. The arrival of trams on Melbourne roads was delayed by lengthy disagreements between the municipalities, the Victorian Government and private interests (Dunstan 1984: ch 8). When these were finally resolved in 1883, the clean, quiet cable tram technology was chosen, no doubt in reaction to Sydney's dirty steam trams. This was an interesting choice as the only other fully developed cable system was in San Francisco. Melbourne subsequently built what was reputedly the world's largest cable network which began operating in 1885. Only eight years later Sydney, after a brief flirtation with cable trams, opted for an electric tram which was installed for a fraction of the capital cost of the cable technology (Cannon 1975: 61). Hobart installed electric trams in 1893, Brisbane in 1896 and Perth in 1899. In Adelaide disagreements between the City Council and surrounding municipalities delayed the changeover from horse drawn to electric trams until 1906. While Melbourne introduced some electric trams, it did not change over completely to the superior technology until 1940. During the inter-war years buses increasingly demonstrated their greater flexibility and effectiveness. Adelaide and Perth ran their last trams in 1958 and Sydney in 1961. Melbourne clung stubbornly to its green monsters for reasons which require fuller investigation. Its trams always had their staunch defenders. When there was a push by other road users for their removal, Chairman Risson of the Tramways Board had the tramlines set in cement, making it far more difficult to remove them.

Sewerage and water supply were two areas where there were more marked differences in the speed with which Australian cities adopted new technologies and where overseas best practice was sometimes not introduced for decades. As the 19th century progressed best practice generally involved the construction of networks in place of decentralised services, for example reticulated water instead of the water tank storing rainwater run-off from the roof, or the water seller. Modern water-flushed sewers were being built in Hamburg, Paris, London and elsewhere in the 1840s and 1850s (Singer 1954: ch 16). Sydney built a limited network which drained into the harbour at various points during the 1860s, and a much larger system with ocean outfalls during the 1880s. Melbourne, with a larger population but a lower population density, made do with cess pits and pans until it finally began building a comprehensive network in 1892. More enlightened Adelaide had begun its system in 1879, while Brisbane with the same population as Adelaide did not connect its first house to its sewers until 1923.

From the outset water supply and sewerage were usually made the responsibility of municipalities who too often did not have the rate base to raise or service the borrowings required to build large dams or sewers. This meant that unlike gas or electricity or trams, water and sewerage were beyond the reach of the urban entrepreneurs who were elsewhere taking risks and introducing new technologies. They were also outside the play of market forces. Consumers who were accustomed to water and sewage disposal which however inadequate, had cost them little or nothing, seem to have been reluctant to pay more. Furthermore a reliance on water and sewerage rates rather than a user pays system was seen more as a tax than a payment, a fact that politicians were acutely aware of when deciding on how much to invest in pan collections, sewer pipes or dams. The process of infrastructure provision in the area of water management can be seen as a story of the reluctant moves to increasingly sophisticated, capital intensive and costly systems once initially cheaper alternatives had palpably failed.

Two kinds of explanations have been advanced to account for the timing of change. In a case study of the costs of economic growth in Melbourne, Sinclair has argued that the community acted rationally in switching to underground sewers once the costs of the existing pan system had risen to a point where it was just as expensive as the technically superior alternative (Sinclair 1975). Case studies of United States cities support this argument (Anderson 1977; Tarr & McMichael 1976). Other explanations have stressed political economy rather than economics. Decisions had to be made by public bodies and these were made when those interests wanting change had grown powerful enough to win the day. This was usually when doctors and public health experts convinced enough people of the escalating social costs of antique systems, mainly in the shape of rising death rates from dirt related diseases. This became somewhat easier as the germ theory was more widely accepted and clean cities demonstrably reduced their death rates

(Dunstan 1985). The two explanations are not mutually exclusive, as Sinclair recognised, but case studies of Sydney, Melbourne and Newcastle, indicate that cost considerations were only one element in the decision-making process (Coward 1988; Lloyd, Troy & Schreiner 1992; Dunstan 1984: ch 9; Dingle and Rasmussen 1991; Frost 1991).

The general conclusion from these studies is that change can be linked to growing externalities, which were, in turn, largely a function of increased city size, although the peculiarities of local geography determined what was technically feasible and therefore the costs of improved systems. At a time when ocean outfalls were regarded as an ideal form of disposal, Melbourne could only envy Sydney for the closeness of the ocean. However, when Melbourne did finally build a system, cost considerations dictated secondary treatment in a sewerage farm at Werribee. Sydney meanwhile, in a classic example of path dependence, has continued to pour its wastes in the ocean largely untreated, despite obvious evidence that some of its waste regularly returns to the beaches and shallow waters to extract retribution (Beder 1989).

III   Public and Private Spheres

In addition to transfers of European technology, Australia and other regions of new settlement required European capital and labour to participate in the world economy. A particular requirement was the development of efficient transportation to link primary producers with European markets, and this was largely done through the actions of government, which organised and released scarce resources of capital and labour. A pragmatic partnership developed between the public and private sector, with the former using its resources to make initial large-scale investments in basic infrastructure, which the latter would have found risky and unprofitable given problems of high land transport costs and isolation from the major sources of capital and labour. Private investment was then expected to follow, with the proceeds of the subsequent growth being shared between the state (through increased revenue from taxes and charges) and the general community (through greater economic activity). In Australia this was known as "colonial socialism", or, after Federation, "state socialism".

The foremost objective of colonial or state socialism was to increase the rural population, through such policies as railway building and the development of large-scale irrigation works (Frost 1992). However, the same principle applied to the development of urban infrastructure networks, with the state using its resources to make investments with scale economies to solve urban problems and thus encourage private investment. The issue of electricity supply illustrates the point. Before the First World War, power generation and transmission was small-scale, with a mixture of public and private enterprises. As systems were converted to public ownership, the building of very large plants and long-distance transmission provided economies of scale (Butlin, Barnard & Pincus 1982: 251-8). The increased scale of power generation permitted greater household electricity use and played an important part in the development of new industries during the interwar years. Protective tariffs stimulated local industries producing domestic electrical appliances and encouraged overseas companies to produce in Australia to avoid tariff barriers. Large-scale power generation was to the advantage of the big cities: in Victoria, the location of coal deposits to the southeast of Melbourne in Gippsland meant that provincial cities like Ballarat, Bendigo and Geelong have to bear higher charges than Melbourne because of greater transmission costs (Bate 1993: 34). Cheap power enhanced the economies of scale in metropolitan centres and between 1921 and 1947 almost half of the new factory jobs in Australia were created in Sydney or Melbourne (Commonwealth Census 1921, 1947).

The use of electricity for industry and transport, together with the internal combustion engine, brought about a major decentralisation of jobs and housing in Australian cities after the First World War. The application of electricity to public transport brought a significant increase in speed and power and allowed the big cities to open up new peripheral suburbs and industrial areas. Between 1902 and 1926 Sydney's tram network was extended and electrified. Then the city's rail services were improved and electrified. New suburban houses created a demand for consumer durables such as cars and electrical appliances, which helped to sustain boom conditions during the 1950s and 1960s. The introduction of television in the late 1950s continued a trend towards suburbanisation of leisure which had begun in the 1920s with the purchase of radios and the building of suburban picture theatres.

IV   Conclusion

Technological change has both affected, and been affected by, Australian urbanisation. On the one hand, the urbanisation of Australia, and the world economic system of which Australia was a part, stimulated technological change and provided greater possibilities for economic growth. Urban markets, production inputs and commercial services encouraged people to adopt overseas best practices or to modify or invent new practices and methods which were suited to Australian conditions. These new technologies were generally adopted quickly once their effectiveness could be demonstrated. On the other hand, networks of sanitation and public transport allowed growing cities to cope with externalities and rising costs. These were provided by a mixture of private enterprise, municipal and colonial (later, State) governments and the nature and standard of investment varied according to political, geographical and planning constraints. The way in which a given urban problem was tackled was often affected by the way in which that problem had been tackled in the past.

By the end of the 19th century Australia's major cities were characterised by significant variations in their spatial structure and quality of infrastructure. Thus while Adelaide was a spacious city with a model system of sewage treatment, Sydney was served poorly by public transport, had large areas of high density housing and disposed of sewage by draining it, untreated, into the Harbour and later to the Pacific. In the 20th century, greater involvement by the State has resulted in economies of scale which have led to a more uniform standard of infrastructure provision. The new areas of factories and housing opened up by public investment in power generation and public transport differ little from city to city. In both Sydney and Melbourne, the term "western suburbs" has the same connotations. Some infrastructural differences persist — Sydney still discharges untreated sewage, for instance — but public ownership and investment has tended to obliterate many of the fine differences between Australian cities. Now that Australian cities have all modern conveniences, they are physically more stereotyped than they have been in the past.

Chapter 2

TRANSPORT TECHNOLOGY AND URBAN DEVELOPMENT

Ray Brindle

Transport and land use are intimately linked, and this interrelationship can not only explain cities historically but can also be used to direct future urban growth.

So commonplace is the above sort of statement that most people (certainly most town planners) would not think to question it. But it is a sort of curate's reality: it is true only in parts. The purpose of this chapter is to encourage the reader to adopt a sceptical view about the conventional wisdom about transport and urban growth, and to think more critically about what aspects of transport (if any) are truly important in urban development compared with the other factors being discussed in this book.

The matter is of current importance, because considerations of the role of transport in visions of the sustainable city (typified by the interesting papers in *Built Environment* 1992 vol 18, no 4) have led inevitably to a revival of proposals to manipulate urban structure (local and regional) to reduce car travel, both through shortening trip lengths (chiefly through *reurbanisation*, or increases in population density) so that powered modes are not required, and the placement of activities so that many trips transfer to non-auto modes. Such proposals reflect the two essential underpinnings of the urban theories apparently most strongly influencing current planning thinking: a belief in our ability to manipulate urban structure to achieve social, environmental or other goals, and a belief that land use-transport relationships are able to be understood and predicted on the basis of macroscopic information. As the author discusses elsewhere (Brindle 1992), there are strongly drawn lines of disagreement about the validity of these beliefs, and hence there are widely divergent views on the feasibility and effectiveness of such actions. While this chapter inevitably reflects on the issue of sustainable urban development, its focus is much more tightly defined. We are concerned here with the extent to which transport technological changes have played a role in urban change, not the pros and cons of different transport policies in the search for ways to reduce greenhouse emissions. Those wishing to explore the transport implications of sustainable development could refer to Breheny (1992), Owens (1986), and Newman (1992b) among many others.

We should start with some definitions and clarifications. This is a discussion about technology, so this chapter will try to be consistent in meaning *transport technology* when the word *transport* is used. *Technology* will generally refer to broad descriptions of modal types and networks, rather than the more ambitious subject of individual vehicle technologies and system control technologies, though the latter will receive a passing mention later on. We should try to avoid the common habit of using the word *transport* when *accessibility, mobility* or *movement* is meant. Loosely, *accessibility* refers to the "intensity of possible interaction" (Hansen 1959: 73), ie degree of proximity to, or relative ease of getting to, urban opportunities such as schools, health services, shops, work and other people. It is an attribute of a place. *Mobility* refers to an individual's ability to move. It is therefore an attribute of a person. *Movement* is the expression of this mobility in response to the existing degree of accessibility to things that people want to get to.

The distinction is important, because much of the urban debate centres (quite properly) on whether transport should serve accessibility or merely cater for increasing demands for mobility. By *transport planning* do we mean mobility planning or access planning — or (as often seems the case) simply infrastructure planning with no real understanding of the link between the infrastructure, accessibility and movement? In the present context, the reader should be clear about the difference when forming opinions about the nature of the role of transport in shaping cities. We could start this discussion with the hypothesis that any interaction between transport (technology) and land use must therefore be through the induced changes in accessibility that arise from land use or transport rearrangements. The chapter will conclude that, while this appears to have been true historically, the effect is progressively weakening as accessibility and mobility both increase dramatically.

It should also be made clear that this is definitely not a discourse on transport policy, planning or needs. What *ought* to happen is different from observing what did and does happen. In particular, readers might be disappointed that the chapter does not pay enough attention to the transport needy, or to questions of equity. While these are subjects of great importance in the planning of urban services and infrastructure, it is argued here that the transport disadvantaged, almost by definition, have not been a major factor in the impacts of transport technology on urban change — certainly not since a very large proportion of society did acquire relatively high levels of personal mobility. The situation described in the chapter may not be popular or a good basis for public policy, nor should it be taken as an indication of the author's preferences. This does not negate the relevance of the evidence brought to support the conclusion in response to the brief for the chapter, which was to explore the influence of the prevailing transport technology on the development of cities.

Several comments on drafts of this chapter observed the relevance of complexity theory to this subject. As a planner rather than an economist or social theorist, I have focused on the land use-transport relationship, generally at the macroscopic level. Other perspectives may have shed a different light on the topic, and almost certainly would have a better chance of explaining some of the mechanisms that will be observed.

I   The Historical Relationship Between Transport and Cities

Cities have been generators of transport technology innovations, as in many other ways. Railways sprang originally as inter-urban links, and trams (as we shall see) gained their impetus as facilitators in the process of suburban land development. The origins of the automobile are rather more complex; it is possibly truer to say that the city responded to the car rather than created it. It is this response of cities to transport (rather than the reverse) to which we now turn.

1   Location

There is ample evidence of the importance of regional location (hence accessibility) in the *siting* of cities in history (Mumford 1961b; Lay 1992). Countless cities found their genesis in the crossing of transport routes, river crossings, sheltered harbours, and (in more modern times) railheads. As fascinating as this subject is, it is not our concern here. However, one aspect of city location does carry hints for the way we should examine growth and change of the cities themselves. Cities came into existence not merely because two tracks crossed, or because there was a good harbour. Rather, depending on the culture and era, town location was principally influenced by various combinations of religious significance, strategic location for military purposes, access to natural resources (including food and water), position relative to regional markets and international trade routes, and many other such factors. Transport, of course, was often the means by which many such accessibilities were achieved. But the transport facility was merely a means to an end; without the right social, military, commercial or human survival imperatives, the location is no more special than anywhere else.

The relevance of this to urban transport and development is that, likewise, mere provision of a form of infrastructure without social or commercial value or logic will not of itself create a predictable type and intensity of urban development. Some examples will be mentioned later. At this point, the reader is warned to be wary of blind faith in *physical determinism* — the widely held but disputed belief that a given urban physical environment will produce a desired social outcome, including the confidence that a given form of transport will create a given form of urban development. This could be described as the *Field of Dreams* syndrome: if you build it, they will come. While the following material will show that transport (particularly the coming of railways and tramways, and the later widespread availability of the car) often had the effect of reinforcing urban expansion, there was no inevitability about it. Establishing the level and nature of causality between components of the urban system is central to the theme of the book, and is as critical to sorting out the realities of transport and urban development as in any other of the accompanying topics.[1]

2   Transport networks and urban change

Having been alerted to some rather negative points, we are now ready to look objectively at the historical role of transport in urban growth through some case studies. Details of the growth and transition of road and rail networks in Australian cities, and the evolution of various types

---

1   On the subject of causality, as we were always warned by our statistics teachers, correlations (such as those between density and trip length, travel mode and energy consumption) do not necessarily establish causation, as Newman (1992) concedes. In any case, the apparent strength of relationships may be misleading, no matter how logical may seem the conceptual relationship. Note particularly that a correlation between population density and any travel parameter *per head* is dominated by the relationship between population and its inverse, and is thus "spurious" (see Brindle 1994). Readers are encouraged to think of possible intermediate variables that may explain the consistent co-occurrence of lower densities and high car usage, and to ponder on whether this co-occurrence truly amounts to "dependency" or not.

of vehicles and transport services, can be found in a number of sources (eg Manning 1991; Neutze 1981: 20-31) and will not be explored here.

Two cases (Perth, Western Australia, and Los Angeles) will be summarised to illustrate typical historical development in new-world cities, and some relevant conclusions from the URBINNO program will be noted. This will be followed by some observations on the role or otherwise of transport technology in urban change as reflected by the cities under consideration.

i   Perth, Western Australia

Selwood notes that, although Perth's first length of passenger rail was not opened until 1881 (between Perth and Guildford), and its impact was not immediate, nevertheless "by the turn of the century Perth had begun to develop the axial pattern of growth tied in to the railways, typical of western industrialised cities" (1979: 428). The line to Fremantle prompted the re-subdivision of many suburban lots in Subiaco, Cottesloe and Buckland Hill into smaller lots, and employment related to the port and railway grew at North Fremantle. Selwood continues:

> With the continued outward spread of population along the railway line, more new stations were added... A significant factor encouraging real estate activity east of Perth was the growth of Midland as a railway centre. (1979: 429)

Tramways were, as in many other places, even more blatantly connected with land development in Perth's suburbs. In 1902, for example, the Oxford Street (Leederville) line was extended along Scarborough Beach Road to Main Street, Osborne Park, under finance from the owners of the large Osborne Park Estate. In 1907:

> [A]n absentee landowner, Colonel Bruce, offered to finance the (Subiaco to Crawley) line's construction so as to provide his holdings on the foreshores of Melville Water at Crawley with good transportation access to the city. (Selwood 1979: 434)

Registration of subdivisions at Osborne Park and Subiaco occurred in the same year as permission was given to tramway construction. As a result of such services, "extensive subdivision occurred in areas not previously available for urban development" (Selwood 1979: 435). Selwood notes also the blurring of the truth by developers about the likelihood of tram services to estates they were selling; even the promise of tram access was enough. Bus services, on the other hand, almost entirely followed rather than helped to generate suburban development. Selwood concludes:

> Public transportation has been an important factor in the evolving development pattern of the Metropolitan Region. However, whatever the transport mode, whatever the ownership and whatever the period, the relationship between transportation and development has been similar. While transportation has reinforced the direction of growth, it has not been the sole, or necessarily even the principal, determinant. (1979: 442)

ii   Los Angeles

Everyone knows that cars and freeways caused the sprawl of Los Angeles. Or did they? Lay claims that: "Los Angeles – the epitome of the suburban city – began to expand under the influence of its electric tram system well before the car had its opportunity to exert an influence" (1992: 307).

Detailed evidence to support this apparently incongruous statement is given by Wachs, a long-time professor of urban planning at UCLA, who explains that "freeways were as much a response to decentralisation as its cause" (1984: 297). Wachs notes the combination of factors that contributed to the low density character of Los Angeles, which "was recognisable before 1900 and well established by 1930" (1984: 297). These were: the tram system, the role of real estate speculators, the special nature of the region's economy and the timing of the region's period of most rapid growth — the 1920s, in which decade, says Wachs, "today's most complex decisions about land use, highways and transit all have their roots" (1984: 297).

Unlike many of the eastern States cities that were introducing streetcars in the late 1800s, Los Angeles had never developed a strong central core before streetcars arrived. Its growth from a mere 5000 population in 1870 to nearly 320,000 in 1910 coincided with the introduction of streetcars and inter-urban rail. As in so many other places, the land speculators exploited the new technology while opening up the cheap land in outlying suburbs and villages which the new arrivals (seeking the good life in the sun) were after. The suburbs were seen as the solution to all sorts of urban ills, and the migrants from the eastern States were unlikely to choose the congested inner urban environments from which they had just escaped. In the first decade of the century, Los Angeles built the largest system of electric railways in the country. Their major amalgamation into the Pacific Electric System provided 1870 kilometres of single track extending more than 160 kilometres from one end to the other by 1923. The Los Angeles Railways company ran a further 500 kilometres of single track within the city itself. The transit companies were active land developers; the Pacific Electric Railway Company developed 13 new towns serviced by its system before 1920. Beverley Hills was among those communities springing from the rail system (Lay 1992: 307). Wachs quotes Crump:

> Unquestionably it was the electric interurbans which distributed the population over the countryside during the century's first decade and patterned Southern California as a horizontal city rather than one of skyscrapers and slums. (Wachs 1984: 300)

The mild climate of Southern California also played a role. Given the exposed nature of most cars available before 1920, it is perhaps not surprising that residents of Los Angeles took to the car more quickly than those elsewhere (one car to nine people in 1919). The roads were also generally in better condition, due to the dry climate. Constraints on growth were eased when the Owens Valley aqueduct was built before 1920 and the city was then on the brink of a second and most rapid surge of development. During that decade after the First World War, "the low density, single family lifestyle that has come to be identified with this city was solidified" (1984: 302), notes Wachs. The population of the City of Los Angeles grew from 577,000 to 1,240,000 and that of the County from 1.2 million to 2.2 million. Most of these were internal migrants; only 20 per cent of Los Angeles residents in 1930 were born in California. The population was more affluent, older and more travelled than urban Americans generally.

The 1920s were a period of active regional planning and economic dispersion in the Los Angeles area. This dispersion sprang from a multiplicity of peculiar local factors which combined to give Los Angeles the pattern which still persists in essence today. For example, the city was under an earthquake precaution ordinance dating from 1906 which limited the height of buildings to 150 feet. This persisted until the mid-1950s, the only exception being the City Hall. This constraint naturally made the core area less attractive to developers than it might have been. Ironically, the surge of downtown development that followed the removal of the height restriction coincided with the peak of freeway construction.

The city planning movement was gaining momentum at the same time. Competing promoters of growth and supporters of the *city beautiful* movement both agreed that the high densities and congestion of the eastern States cities should be avoided. The philosophies and actions of the Regional Planning Commission (formed in 1923, the first in the United States) actively dissuaded central city living and working, and promoted dispersal of both. A major road plan to support this dispersed pattern was prepared in 1923 whose influence on Los Angeles is evident today, but clearly it would be a gross over-simplification to say that the car (much less the post-war freeways) were the primary cause of Los

Angeles' form and structure. At the same time, it was assumed that transit would also be essential. However, a rapid transit plan of 1925 was substantially rejected by voters through a number of factors, including public disapproval of the propping up of the private transit company which had a poor record of service, and the association of the transit plan with "crooked politicians, kickbacks and land grabs" (Wachs 1984: 309). The plan also contained 140 kilometres of elevated route, which was seen as intrusive. As a result, a transit plan had not been adopted by the time the Depression arrived, and an opportunity was lost.

Wachs states that it was this combination of circumstances, "rather than a clear preference for automobiles" (1984: 309), that led to the adoption of a highways plan but not a transit plan in the 1920s. Even so, the 3 million or so Los Angeles (City) residents in 1980 were living at 30 per hectare gross, according to data collected by Newman and Kenworthy (1989), which is more than double the gross figure calculated for Australian cities and of the same order as that for many European suburban areas. It is also the target density commonly promoted for sustainable Australian urban areas, particularly for *efficient* public transport. We should not jump to rash conclusions about either the nature of Los Angeles or the factors which caused it.

iii   Conclusions from the URBINNO Project

A principal source for students of influences on change in urban form and structure can be found in the outputs of the URBINNO project. URBINNO — Innovation and urban development: the role of social and technological change — set out to analyse the influence of innovation and technological development in the process of urbanisation since about 1850. Giannopoulos and Curdes (1992) report the studies of eight European cities, representing three types and various stages of growth and economic evolution, to answer questions which included: "How far does transport innovation influence urban form?"

Referring to the impacts of the car on the physical characteristics of older central areas, Giannopoulos and Curdes state that the car has "undoubtedly had, and continues to have, a greater effect on urban form than any other single mode of transport" (1992: 26). The difference between older European and the new-world cities is apparent, and is probably related to the relative rates of growth into non-urban land. Even so, the role of streetcars in creating the suburbs, as in the cases from the United States and Australia, is apparent from the study. The different (and therefore unpredictable) effects of similar measures in different cities was noted. The authors conclude:

> All transport innovations have influenced the form and extent of the development of the urban area examined, but none of them has determined that form completely . . . the influence of innovations on urban form is high in an early stage of development and lower in dense and built-up towns. (Giannopoulos & Curdes 1992: 28-9)

3   Observations on the role of transport technology

The pattern is commonplace: fixed rail systems were typically levers for dispersed suburban development, and in fact thrived on that dispersal until the growth in car availability. (That fact alone should make us stop and think about the need to increase densities in order to support public transport. The 1950s rail-dependent suburbs of Sydney and Melbourne are, if anything, more closely built up today than they were 40 years ago, yet public transport use is much lower. What else has changed, and what does that mean for the importance given to density in modal planning?).[2]

Lay concludes that:

> [I]t cannot be said that the train or the tram or the car or the freeway caused the urban sprawl of both housing and industry, for they were all easily predated by that sprawl. Clearly, factors far larger than transport have been at work, and it would be wrong to see cities as merely the passive consequences of transport developments. . . Nevertheless, the role of transport in aiding and abetting the process was significant. (1992: 306)

Lay goes on to list what he calls the "real transport villains . . . but the real catalyst (for urban expansion) from 1880 to 1914 was the electric tram" (1992: 306).

As an aside, it may be argued that the involvement of land developers in transit expansion and operation was beneficial because it provided us with today's infrastructure. This is certainly true; in more subtle ways, provision of much of Melbourne's extensive rail network involved more than a touch of self-interest (Cannon 1964). Cynics might respond that the manipulation of the urban growth process that ensued

---

2   In 1861, about half Melbourne's population lived in municipalities whose gross density was 20 per hectare or less. Neutze (1981) shows that this dropped to about one-third by 1891 and was 8 per cent in 1976. "Even these figures underestimate residential densities", he points out. The discrepancy between these figures and those used with such profound effect by Newman and Kenworthy (1989), who cite Melbourne's gross density in 1980 as 16.4 per hectare, should alert the reader to be careful when interpreting data and propositions related to population density and travel. See McLoughlin (1991) and Mees (1995).

was all in the developer's favour. Typically, the companies ran down or withdrew from transit services as patronage and income dropped, and their profits from land development were achieved. The public sector was then left with large networks and increasing subsidies. Note that the fascination of land developers with trams is alive and well. The promotion of Canberra's Northbourne Avenue tram by land developers as an *essential* part of the Gungahlin Urban Village (*A New Vision for Canberra* 1992) had its precedents in the actions and advertisements of developers 80-100 years ago.[3] How do we determine the long-term effects and appropriateness of such proposals? Conventional travel demand analyses are unlikely to give us the whole story.

To take that case even further, those puzzled by a preference for a Northbourne Avenue streetcar — with its inevitably slower travel times compared with car travel — rather than a genuine rapid transit link, should perhaps examine St Kilda Road (Melbourne) and contemplate where the real commercial investment potential will lie in Canberra. It is not too bold a prediction to expect that the principal effect of such a facility will be to pull central functions northwards from Civic and to precipitate demand for major commercial redevelopment, perhaps along the whole length of Northbourne Avenue. Experienced transport planners know that, when the private sector enthusiastically promotes a specific transport facility, property development or other commercial incentives are often lurking in the background. One does not have to commit the heresy of suggesting that this is not necessarily a good thing; it is sufficient merely to point out that history should warn us to be alert both to the longer-term viability of the transport facility and to the commercial opportunities which it will unlock, not all of which will have socially and economically desirable effects. Here is a pointer to a more pragmatic understanding of the effects of transport on urban change.

The underlying reality, which explains our difficulties in manipulating urban systems especially through transport infrastructure, is that the historical influences on the urban system are very complex and we need to understand the lever that transport technology may or may not have on that complex system. Further, as Giannopoulos and Curdes observe:

> [T]owns are socio-physical systems with a high stability and resistance to short-term transformations. Any urban morphology has its own logic,

---

3   Note in passing Handy's (1992) observation that high regional accessibility tends to work against high local accessibility, a subject also approached, but in a different way, by Headicar (1991). A high-capacity transport system to an "urban village" will almost guarantee low local satisfaction of trip desires.

pattern and scale. Technical innovations have short life cycles in relation to the permanence of an urban morphology. (1992: 28)

The combination of new technology and the unique existing conditions in a city creates a synthesis which is compatible (by definition) with that particular urban system. The outcome might be quite different in a different urban context, or if the cycles come in different phases.

Meyer and Gómez-Ibáñez (1981) underline the point in their discussion of Toronto, which is frequently quoted as a model of transit-land use interdependence (Kenworthy 1991). Yet in their review of several econometric studies of Toronto's development, Meyer and Gómez-Ibáñez conclude cautiously that the subway system "did have a major impact on the distribution and intensity of development, though not as much as many proponents claimed" (1981: 117). The evidence, they said, showed that the transit system was not the single cause of the observed land use effects, but that rather a "variety of economic and social factors" (1981: 117), including unusually high European immigration, combined to create higher transit use and land use changes. It should be noted also that the Toronto Transit Commission had played a developer-type role in facilitating the concentration of land development at key nodes, thus evoking the role of the land developer-transit company of the past without the profit component. Meyer and Gómez-Ibáñez concluded that any controlled impact of transport on land development tends to be:

> [O]n a limited or local scale and most effective when coordinated, as in Toronto, with other public policies... Furthermore, if there is no underlying demand for higher-density development, then almost no combination of public policies will elicit a more compact urban structure in a modern market economy. (1981: 121)

More importantly, they observed that "transportation system changes can affect land use in distant as well as neighbouring areas" (1981: 116), raising the need to be aware of wider systematic changes than simply those at the focus of attention. There are very strong indications that Toronto's excellent transit system and promotion of suburban sub-centres, when combined with the ability to exercise high levels of personal mobility by car found in that city, in fact helps to stretch rather than compress the home-to-work and other linkages. A similar phenomenon, on a regional scale, was recounted to the author in the United Kingdom. Patronage on a commuter rail line in southeast England was double that expected because of rapid population growth caused by people taking advantage of the transport service to improve their living environment. As central area jobs declined, commuter belt residents took local jobs which required them to drive to work. Thus, an increase in public transport accessibility had in the end led to an increasing car usage because of exogenous economic changes out of the planners' control (or at least outside their awareness).

II But Hang On —

Does all this contradict what Britton Harris (1961) described long ago as an "instinctive feeling" that transport is a key element in urban planning? The answer is an emphatic *no* — clearly, the *planning* of land use and transport should be in tune with each other. But the usual assumption is that this is so simply because the two intimately interact and are mutually deterministic. The subject was commonplace during the 1960s, such that by the end of that decade it was possible to observe that "many, if not all, transport engineers acknowledge that such an interaction exists" (Brindle 1970b: 8). The writings of Mitchell in the United States (Mitchell 1959; Mitchell & Rapkin 1964) had been influential in reinforcing this understanding.

Despite all the foregoing, we *can* describe cities historically at least partly in terms of the transport technology available to them. Perhaps the most apt source in the present context arises from ten years of research at the Urban Research Unit of the Australian National University:

> The effects of the transport system on the spread of the city at different periods can explain many of the features of modern cities. Until the mid-1850s transport within Australian cities and towns was on foot, or by horse or bullock wagon, except in those few locations served by boat. . . Because most people walked, cities developed as compact settlements. (Neutze 1981: 20)

The theme is commonplace, as for example in Newman (1992b) and in the report of the International Study Group on Land-use/Transport Interaction:

> Initially, cities were generally restricted to a size at which most of their inhabitants could walk from one part to another, and in the larger cities this often caused people to live at remarkably high densities. This highly concentrated lifestyle produced serious social stresses in the rapidly growing industrial cities of the nineteenth century, a situation which was considerably improved when the introduction of mechanised public transport allowed people to spread themselves along the service routes, where they could live at lower densities yet still have ready access by bus or rail to the central workplaces. In the last few decades, the advent of mass car ownership has allowed development to take place at still lower densities and in a more dispersed manner.

This intricate connection between land use and transport means that any policy, whether relating specifically to land-use development or to the provision of transport facilities, will inevitably affect the other dimension, though not necessarily on the same timescale. (Webster, Bly & Paulley 1988: 4)

As Neutze points out: "Car ownership allowed people to live away from public transport routes" (1981: 26) just as rail had allowed people to live away from the city centres. Extrapolated into modern times, the impact of transport planning on urban form was widely recognised, at least in broad terms. The report of the Adelaide transportation study of the 1960s, for example, stated heroically that one of the "cardinal rules" was that "the physical impact of the transportation system on the metropolitan area itself must be acceptable to the community" (MATS 1966: 7) — heroic because they had absolutely no means by which the impact of the network on the city and its travel behaviour could be anticipated. Like all other transportation studies of that time, the Adelaide study started with "a precise picture of Metropolitan Adelaide for the next twenty years" (MATS 1966: 11), that is, *before* the future transport network had been identified. As this author pointed out at the time (while already showing more than a touch of reservation about the nature of the interaction between land use and transport):

> The dependence of transport demand on land development patterns is evident...The converse relationship — the partial dependence of the type and density of development in an area on the quality and proximity of transport facilities — is widely accepted but is not easy to prove or quantify. (Brindle 1970b: 5)

The key to reconciling this mass of apparent contradictions lies in the frequent use of the word *allow*, which points us back to the difference between accessibility and movement. Simply, the availability of a particular technology may be a necessary but is rarely a sufficient pre-condition for a specific urban change. As in several other topics in this collection, the word *enabling* is pertinent. The role of transport in urban development is moving from a deterministic to a permissive status. Thus, the interpretation of a *relationship* between land use, transport and energy consumption as a one-to-one *dependency* is not valid. The overwhelming conclusion from the literature in fact is that transport rarely, in itself, causes a predictable and significant change in urban development — certainly not to the extent that we could rely on it as a policy tool. As Klaasen put it, "Of the nature of the interaction and its progress through time not much is known for certain" (1990: 9). The reality is that:

> We are very good at establishing the transport consequences of particular patterns of city development... We are *not* very good at translating transport characteristics into estimated impacts on land use, for example the extent to which high quality public transport concentrates activity at key points in the system. We know it happens, from experience around the world, but we do not know how to forecast its extent nor even what mechanisms we need to establish to make sure it happens. (Ker 1991: 35)

In other words, Ker and many other commentators are saying that we need to know more about mechanisms of change in cities if we are to understand the relationship between transport technology and urban change. A starting point is the relationship between the pattern of urban activities (land use), accessibility and degree of ease of movement.

III   The Land Use-Accessibility-Mobility Relationship

The issue is not "Is there a relationship between transport and land use?", because the answer is patently in the affirmative. In the face of crucial problems facing cities and the globe, we need to know how we can interpret and manipulate this relationship. In working from the copious literature on this subject, the implied determinism has to be interpreted carefully. How can we come to grips with this issue?

A clue came from Nicholas Clark at a time when these things were being discussed with a lot more sense of enquiry than they are now:

> A city is not the land it occupies nor the buildings and material things erected on that land. A city is a social and economic system. It is the activities that occur within that system that create the demand for the use of land and buildings and their construction. The present land use strategy plan and previous town plans (for Melbourne) have been preoccupied with the latter, with the physical expressions of human activity and not with those activities themselves. Land and buildings are only two of the resources used by people in urban living. (1972: 20)

In essence, a given land use pattern sets an accessibility pattern for a given level of mobility and transport availability. But that is not enough to explain the travel outcome. If it were, the relatively simple gravity-based concepts of travel demand and distribution would suffice (Hansen 1959). But we have to contend with the socio-economic characteristics that help to determine the individual decisions to build at a particular place, or to select a job somewhere, or to travel by a particular route or mode. This matter is flagged here without much more expansion, being a major topic outside our present brief. We should, however, give a little more thought to the role played by accessibility in urban decisions.

A helpful discussion is found in Headicar, who points out:

The changes in urban form which have occurred during the period of motorisation are themselves but a part of a still longer process of interaction between land use and transport which centres on changes in accessibility. (1991: 7)

Headicar notes the eventual loss in accessibility, due to congestion (road or rail), of the central area. At the same time, other differentiations in the accessibility surface arise when there is heavy transport investment in selected corridors. Methods commonly used to anticipate the effects of transport on urban change implicitly assume that this change in the accessibility surface will have a direct effect on locational, and hence travel, decisions. But two significant trends in the latter half of this century make this less certain and predictable than it might have been:

1. As we noted earlier, the effect of increasing car availability has meant that urban dwellers with access to motor vehicles, under present pricing and demand management structures, have very flexible levels of mobility. This in turn means that, within very broad limits, they are far less constrained in their choice of home location or, conversely, in their choice of activities from a given dwelling. For example, a lawyer living in Ringwood in Melbourne could equally well have her/his office in the city or in Bayswater. Her/his children may go the local secondary college, or (more likely) to a private school in Hawthorn. Her/his partner's dental practice could be in Yarra Glen or Glen Waverley. She/he prefers a hairdresser in Camberwell, because that's where she/he has gone for years. They could go to church round the corner or to a fashionable inner-city church. Their son, if he plays soccer, will expect to be able to travel to away games from Geelong to Frankston. They may be in a theatre group that rehearses in Monbulk. Very likely, they have a country retreat 90 minutes drive away.

    This is not entirely a caricature. It is a familiar sketch of many, if not most, suburban households, certainly in terms of how widely they range across the urban area for all their activities. The study of these linkages (*urban spatial dynamics*) is central to understanding the role of transport in urban change. It always has been, but especially so as more of the population moved into the more mobile socio-economic groups and (at least as far as those who make the influential urban decisions are concerned) suburban areas moved towards what seems, for all practical purposes, to be a state of ubiquitous travel for all and hence effectively constraint-free accessibility to all locations. The ultimate implications of such a trend are rather gloomily foreshadowed in Headicar's last two sentences:

> In the long run the process of motorisation will be complete and the pattern of activity and development will have altered so that no basis of transportation other than the private car will be practical. In the long run there will be no choices left to be decided on.(1991: 26)

In the limit, if we travelled by teleporting then no location would be any more advantageous than any other in terms of travel. Locations (for home, in particular) would be chosen for other attributes. We are closer to that state now than to the constraints of the *walk city*, especially if the communications enthusiasts are to be believed (particularly in view of communications substitutes for work travel), and this must affect our interpretation and application of the historical data.

This phenomenon can be reflected by, for example, the parameter used to indicate the *probability of choice* in intervening opportunities models. Faced with an opportunity to satisfy her/his travel objective at a particular place, what is the probability that a traveller will choose that destination rather than move on to another? In locational terms, similarly, what is the probability that a householder will choose a residential location close to work rather than the next one further out? and so on. Clearly, the higher this probability, the more compact a city will be. Many years ago, the author demonstrated that, for Adelaide at least, this probability has steadily declined over this century, reflecting the gradual freeing up of locational choices and hence greater dispersal of the city as constraints on personal movement eased, mainly through car availability (Brindle 1970a, 1970b). According to this representation of the urban decision process, we cannot simply change the *probability of choice* parameter arbitrarily. It is a characteristic of the city, reflecting the socio-economic characteristics that link accessibility and mobility to travel. Intuitively, we expect to see a trend in the model parameter which corresponds to the dispersal of the city that has occurred. It is worth pointing out, however, that much of the current literature on urban change for sustainability implies a strong localisation of travel and hence a much higher *probability of choice* value than would be derived at present.

2. **The accessibility needs of urban activities have changed:**

> The effect of transport improvements in suburban and peripheral areas is compounded by changes in the locational requirements of the land use activities themselves. These have led to decentralisation and outward expansion over many decades. As a result a much greater proportion of firms and households are now located in, and are most easily accessed from, areas well away from the traditional commercial and industrial core. (Headicar 1991: 7)

As the economy moves more towards services than manufacturing, and communications replaces a proportion of the movement of commodities, dispersal and suburbanisation results because service providers have fewer locational constraints. There are of course ways to restrain this dispersion through planning controls, such as the very interesting Dutch accessibility and mobility profiles (van Huut 1991) which seek to match locations of employment with the level of accessibility they need and the likely mobility of their employees. The dispersion of cities is only partly explained by the fact that such controls have not been widely exercised, or, where they have, they have not been significant in their scope. Conversely, more closely relating of workplaces to employees may help the journey to work, but not the other 75 per cent or so of urban travel. Handy's (1992) study of retail accessibility and shopping travel is not wholly encouraging; other less-structured components of non-work travel are likely to be even less rational and controllable.

IV Communications, Vehicle and System Technology

At this point, discussions on the nature of technology and urban change conventionally move towards a consideration of communications technology. It is with some relief that this author refers the reader to the work of Brotchie (eg Brotchie et al 1985), Hepworth and Ducatel (1992) and Lamberton's contribution to the present volume.

Points to consider when contemplating the effects of new communications technology, especially in relation to how it may change historical understandings of the relationship between transport and urban change, include:

1. **The ability of communications technology to substitute for movement.** The frequent response is that the more mobile in the community are the greatest users of new technologies such as

mobile phones. Also commonly heard is the view that nothing will replace face-to-face contact, the social experience of shopping is something people will still seek, and so on.

2. **Specifically, the effects of communications technology on working at home.** The availability of the technology is not an issue. Rather, questions centre around what percentage of workers will in fact be able to take advantage of *tele-working*.

3. **The effects of dispersal on travel.** Ultimately, will freedom from the need to be relatively near to the workplace have the effect of increasing or decreasing total travel by the household?

Most of the possible developments in *vehicle and system technology* seem likely, if anything, to reinforce the trend to greater mobility and more uniform accessibility, for example:

1. Development of the *benign car*, while clearly not overcoming all the social, safety and other problems of the automobile, may well take the political wind out of the sails of urban change.

2. Merging of *private transport* with *public transport*, for example through Personal Rapid Transit (PRT) guideway networks which also accommodate dual-mode private cabs, could serve both high- and lower-density development and would therefore not be a factor in decisions about urban form and structure. It would, however, reduce the pressure for change generated by considerations of inequities and externalities of present automobiles.

3. Improvements in speed and reliability of service (rail or road) may influence modal choices, and are thus outside our brief here. They may also marginally change the accessibility surface across the urban region and thus have some influence on the distribution of activities.

4. Generally, transport technology changes reinforce the trend towards greater mobility and more uniform accessibility. This is especially true of cross-suburban and circumferential routes or services. Technology is also tending to improve the quality of services and particularly the information given to the traveller.

5. Driver advisory systems such as those currently preoccupying the European DRIVE program also tend, if anything, to support dispersed patterns, by helping to reduce the costs as well as the impacts of journeys.

Readers might like to ponder on other examples of technological development to see if they can think of any changes in transport technology (as distinct from policy or plan) which are likely to be both effective in concentrating cities and reducing travel, and acceptable to the community.

V Conclusions

The explanation of urban change offered here can be summarised thus: The static measure we call *accessibility* is affected by location and quality of transport service. Through its role in determining accessibility (of the city as a whole, and the relative locations within it), transport has clearly been an important factor in the development of urban areas. For the major part of human history, the level of mobility of the mass of the population was low and the accessibility needs of most urban activities were not great. The coming of urban railways and the growth of the middle classes meant that both accessibility and mobility were increased for growing numbers of people. Relative location started to be less important, for householders, employers and even commercial activity. The pressure for dispersal was already there when the railways and electric trams came to provide both the incentive for suburban development and the means to escape to the new Arcadia.[4] The car allowed this trend to continue.

Into modern times, while accessibility is not uniformly good due to congestion and incompleteness of the transport system, the city — at least in respect to residential location decisions — has responded as if accessibility was relatively unimportant. There are two factors contributing to this. First, despite identifiable inequities and unevenness in the distribution of goods and services in cities, there has been a large-scale suburbanisation of most of the things that suburban dwellers and commercial activity need. Secondly, and most crucially, modern urban dwellers have much greater personal mobility than their predecessors, albeit with unrealised costs and cross-subsidies (but that is another story). This chapter has made the point that when people can move relatively freely to anywhere, and when all points are equally accessible, the power of accessibility in shaping cities is broken and dispersal is the inevitable outcome. Social and technological trends have moved us inexorably towards that state.

---

4   Max Lay (1992) tells of the clay tablet which records joy of a Babylonian householder some 2500 years ago with his villa in the countryside away from the noise and bustle of the city, yet with all the benefits of proximity to urban life.

So accessibility — and hence transport technology — has historically been important but is decreasingly so as travel becomes more universal and ubiquitous. If this is so, we must conclude that attempts to reshape cities and reduce travel through the manipulation of the accessibility surface, the transport network, densities and so on are doomed to fail on their own, whatever else such policies may achieve. Here the techniques of travel demand management become important, especially those techniques which aim to price properly the individual's mobility. Increases in travel costs would have the effect of reducing mobility, thus restoring some of the effectiveness of transport infrastructure and activity location in determining locational and movement decisions.

This is not, as some have said, a pessimistic conclusion. It merely suggests that the *Field of Dreams* will only come true if other things happen; we cannot rely solely on a simplified view of the land use-transport relationship to work miracles. Here there is some correspondence with other contributions to this collection, particularly Lamberton's Chapter 4 .

In this discussion, a number of planning issues may have come to mind which cannot be given the attention they deserve in the space available:

1. Reference has been made to those left behind by the *mobility rich* society, and the need for transport planning to acknowledge them. As indicated earlier, this is an important but different subject which does not affect the validity of the interpretation given here of urban change and transport's effect on it.

2. For some contributors to the urban debate, the enforced reduction in mobility is an end in itself. While the theme is outside the subject of this volume, students of urban change will note the sometimes quite overt intention to restrict mobility, at least by private powered modes (as being anti-social or undemocratic). The effect of such policies, if the community were to allow them, would be to increase the importance of accessibility in determining location and travel.

3. The dilemma is that the inexorable trend towards dispersal does not match the centralising, concentrating and corridor character of the familiar linear modes of public transport. The response to this situation may be either to try to shape the city to fit the technology or to seek a technology more appropriate to today's and tomorrow's urban regions and lifestyles. This chapter offers no views on that subject, other than to point out our lack of

success so far in the former course. Possible technologies for 21st century cities are a subject needing separate consideration.

4. The urban transport-land use *system* is one of many that Cartwright describes as being "well understood (in the sense that they can be fully described by means of a finite set of conditions or rules) and yet are fundamentally unpredictable" (1991: 44) — ie it is *chaotic*. Urban analysts need to come to terms with the implications of the concept of "chaos" in trying to understand the role of transport in shaping cities (Gleick 1987). The very concept — order without predictability — throws a cloud of uncertainty over *scientific* approaches to urban planning, including both traditional urban modelling and the macro-level relationships used to underpin the currently popular views of cities and transport (Brindle 1992).

5. Urban freight technology and its influence has received little attention, partly because the author makes no pretence at expertise in that field and partly because, if anything, the mechanisms of change due to freight technology were in all likelihood working in the same direction as those of personal movement. This, however, is an acknowledged gap in this discussion which others will have to fill.

What of the future? While there is copious literature on past urban development based on observations about the relationship between high-capacity transit and certain urban structures, we cannot be sure of successfully using the relationship in reverse — that is, inducing intended structures and travel behaviours by inserting specific transport technologies and services. Extrapolation from past urban development into the 21st Century is an act of nostalgia. Taking us back like time travellers to urban structures and transport technologies of the past could only work if we too became the people we once were, with the same values, incomes lifestyles — and constraints on choices. Urban people today generally have much wider economic, political and social choices than their predecessors. The most successful transport and urban technologies of the near future will be those which cater for this widening choice without the excessive compromising of ecological, resource and social values characterised by the growth in automobility in this century. This implies some form of on-call, not shared, many-to-many but regulated system.

The author has tried to avoid making any value judgements about the desirability of the trends and causes identified here. It is necessary to go beyond treatment of the *symptoms* of urban malaise, and to get to the underlying *causes*, if we are to understand and manipulate cities to our mutual advantage and welfare. In doing so, we need to be careful in interpreting the lessons of history; many of the familiar preconceptions drawn from the past seem to be misleading.

Chapter 3

WATER, SEWERAGE AND DRAINAGE

Clem Lloyd

Cities are captives of their water supply and sewerage disposal systems, but they are not captives of water supply and sewerage technology. This apparent paradox is the basis of the attempt here to analyse the impact of water technology on urban development and form. Briefly, the thesis boils down to four propositions:

1. Urban development is dependent on ready access to sustainable water sources and supplies;

2. Urban form is influenced, sometimes decisively, by the choice of sustainable water sources and supplies;

3. Urban development has been essentially unresponsive to technological change in the water/sewerage/drainage (WSD) industry;

4. While urban form has become more sensitive to technological change in the WSD industry, the consequences are unlikely to be significant in the short to medium term.

It is suggested that the impact of WSD services on urban development and urban form is largely independent of technological change. While technological change will persist, and perhaps quicken, in the WSD industry this will not change the fundamental nature of finding water, storing it, distributing it, and disposing of it after use. The impact of locating and developing water sources will continue to be determined largely by historical factors, particularly the location of major storage and supply networks. This pattern will be accentuated if demand patterns are modified to constrain water use and defer or even eliminate the need for new storage sources and delivery and disposal services. WSD systems are susceptible to modest change and modification from new technology, but certainly not to transformation. While this analysis is based on the Australian experience, much of it is applicable to urbanisation and urban form in the cities of other countries.

I   Australia, WSD and Urban Development

The urban development of Australia dealt harshly with the inherited water cycle. The nation's founders had to establish settlement in a forbidding environment by making the most expedient use of the resources close at hand. Even the rudimentary water treatment and distribution technology available in England when Australian urbanisation began could not be transported adequately to colonial frontiers. The Australian colonies had access, at least for a time, to much purer water stocks than the accustomed standards of Europe. The purity of the original supply, however, was soon sullied by pollution. Increasingly, domestic consumption had to share scarce water supplies with the demands of cultivation, grazing and industry. By the 1820s, the pollution of harbours, estuaries and smaller streams in settled areas was well advanced.

With rising urbanisation, water had to be brought from sources increasingly distant from urban settlement as the initial supplies were expunged or polluted beyond tolerable levels. To their credit, the early governors tried to regulate water usage and prevent pollution from sewage and trade waste, a thankless task. They could not reconcile the fundamental dilemma that water was both an essential consumption good for domestic, farming and industrial use, and also the most effective means of waste disposal. For human consumption and the maintenance of public health, water sources had to be either pure or capable of purification. Use of running water for disposal of human and trade waste polluted sources way beyond the capability of contemporary technology to purify them. Water-borne disease was an inevitable consequence. The first test of technology, particularly engineering technology, was not to find a means of purifying water at these primal sources, but to devise ways of finding and storing water where it could not be contaminated. The technology had then to distribute these stocks of pure water to urban households and industries.

II   Technology and Infrastructure Development

These formidable objectives were achieved by technologies whose fundamentals remain unchanged today: storage dams; headworks; piped distribution networks; piped wastewater disposal networks. For Sydney, sources shifted from the Tank Stream to the northern fringes of Botany Bay, then to the catchments of the Nepean River southwest of initial settlement and, in later years, to the Shoalhaven waters well to the south. Melbourne water supply moved from the Yarra and its tributaries to catchments in the ranges north of the city. More precariously, Adelaide's principal water source shifted to the Murray River some 80 kilometres from the city. Perth's main water sources moved from the coastal plains drained by the Swan River system to catchments in the Darling Ranges overlooking the areas of initial settlement. Brisbane water sources also moved from a coastal river system to catchments in ranges to the west of the city, and Hobart gained permanent supplies from a formidable mountain catchment. Canberra exploited water sources in what were distant mountain catchments, although urban development has brought them somewhat closer in recent years.

These expansions were achieved by huge investment in substantial projects which reflected in ample measure both emergent technology and conventional engineering skills. In many respects, the achievement has been impressive. Storage dams have been soundly constructed, drawing on established technology from Europe and the United States, but with important doses of innovation. Potential defects have been detected well in advance of structural failure and remedial works undertaken. The propensity for major flooding in river systems linked to great storage dams, such as Burrinjuck Dam on the Murrumbidgee and Warragamba Dam on the Nepean system, has aroused spasmodic apprehension but the structures have held. Reticulation systems devised for relatively modest urban development have been amplified to meet the demands of much greater population. Until the 1970s the wastewater disposal systems coped with growing urbanisation but, even with substantial infrastructure investment based on technological advance, sewerage and drainage services have become increasingly straitened over the past 20 years. Technological solutions contrived on the distant catchment philosophy might have worked well enough in isolation, but the universal adoption of waste disposal through water-borne systems has exposed their limitations.

The disposal of waste, both household and trade, was not performed as a major function by Australian water-supply authorities until the late 19th century. State and municipal authorities experimented with a variety of alternatives to water-borne disposal: the traditional household privy or middenstead; municipal collection and burial; municipal sewerage farms; incineration; pneumatic disposal; septic tanks (also known as the American system). As urbanisation flourished, however, an increasing volume of domestic sewage was discharged into crude drainage systems and thence into creeks, rivers and harbours. With the development of municipal drainage, wealthier households and commercial firms were able to make illegal connections to discharge the contents of increasingly effective water closets. The medical profession and emerging public health authorities advocated water-borne sewage disposal as the remedy for typhoid, diphtheria, scarlet fever, dysentery and other maladies linked with water contamination.

As a general panacea the alternatives to water-borne disposal of waste were failures. Certainly, elements of alternative technology were applied for many years in Australian cities. In the years after the Second World War rapid urbanisation depended on municipal collection and burial of human waste — a ritual which persisted into the 1960s. Septic tanks have been ubiquitous in Australian cities for longer periods, with 30 per cent of Perth's coastal suburbs still sewered by a septic system introduced in the early 1900s. Sewerage farms represented something of a half-way house, with much of the sewage arriving by water-borne disposal, but treatment processes combining disposal elements of evaporation and desiccation, as well as the discharge of treated effluent into estuaries and oceans. Human waste collected by the municipalities was either buried, discharged into the sewerage system, or conveyed to sewerage farms where this was convenient. Septic tanks were pumped out sporadically with the residue usually discharged through the sewerage system. It is difficult to estimate to what extent waste from both sources was dumped into creeks, estuaries and oceans although, undoubtedly, such crude disposal did occur.

Sewerage farms made a significant contribution to waste disposal in Australia's cities, particularly in Melbourne where the metropolitan farm at Werribee near Port Phillip Bay southwest of the city was the key-stone of the sewerage system for many years. Generally, the demands for waste disposal by big, modern cities have grown way beyond the capability of sewerage farms, although they remain a useful supplement. Furthermore, the farms make demands on land resources and thus become increasingly vulnerable to urbanisation. Although the farms do not require the elaborate spatial quarantining of water catchments, they become aesthetically unacceptable within metropolitan areas, just as crematoria for burning human waste were rejected by new municipalities in 19th century Australia. Distant sewage farm systems are technologically feasible but require huge levels of infrastructure investment. This is the nub of the argument raised from time to time in Australia for pumping metropolitan sewage large distances for disposal at sparsely occupied inland locations. Unless some commercial value can be obtained from the residue it becomes increasingly difficult to maintain *dry* farming techniques. By the 1990s, the bulk of Australia's sewerage was borne through the WSD system into the ocean.

It is interesting to speculate what might have happened if Australia had been urbanised on the basis of a distant catchment water system unburdened by wastewater disposal. Even if it had been possible to take the S out of the WSD formula, and it has been argued here that this was never a realistic possibility, the D factor would have remained. Drainage is the product of elemental rainwater which largely flows away as wastewater but is capable of being captured, stored and delivered as part of a water supply system. The iron or galvanised iron tank, indeed, is as idiomatic an Australian catchment as the earthen dam. With contemporary water supply systems, only a small part of rainwater is captured and stored for consumption. The remainder is either absorbed into the soil, evaporates or has to be disposed of through technologically based water systems as drainage water which is sullied by run-off over soil and degraded by the pick-up of myriad solid elements.

As Australia urbanised, basic drainage services were provided municipally, with local councils adapting natural drainage systems and providing artificial systems, usually in conjunction with a developing network of road and carriageways. As noted earlier, household waste, including excreta, and trade waste were also decanted into municipal drains. Other pollution was picked up by stormwater run-off across household backyards where excrement was buried close to the surface. As roads were hardened with surfaces of gravel, bitumen and concrete, municipal kerbing and guttering advanced in design and use of materials. These more elaborate systems, however, often cut across the natural drainage framework, and problems of run-off were accentuated by the harder surfaces. Municipal systems were rarely integrated, provoking tensions between adjoining councils whose drainage often spilled across municipal boundaries. With increasing urbanisation, the statutory water authorities had little option but to accept an over-riding responsibility for disposal of drainage waters through the provision of trunk drainage systems which transmitted municipal drainage water into the sewerage disposal systems.

Although drainage is virtually as old as water supply in Australia, it has been very much subordinate to water and sewerage services in public policy and infrastructure provision. The division of responsibility between municipal and statutory authorities has contributed to a neglect of drainage services which has only been addressed with the impact of rapid urbanisation on stormwater run-off. Higher water pollution levels and huge strains on sewerage disposal and treatment systems have given drainage a somewhat belated priority in the public policy of WSD.

The great surges of Australia's urbanisation have largely been generated by private sector real estate development sustained by substantial public sector investment in physical and social infrastructure. In recent years charges imposed on developers have recouped part of this public commitment to urban services, including WSD. In total, such reimbursement has not had an enormous revenue effect and the thrust of urbanisation has been heavily underwritten from the public purse. The public sector has also provided public housing programs which have contributed to rapid urban growth over more than 40 years, particularly on successive urban fringes receding into the hinterland.

Australia's urbanisation, particularly since the Second World War, has been predicated on the basis of ready access to cheap water of high quality. Earlier investments in storage dams and headworks sufficed to provide such a water supply to the new suburbs, except in Adelaide where lower quality water standards were tolerated until relatively recent years. Unquestionably, Australia's urbanisation owes much to the quality of its hydrologists and hydraulic engineers. It is a remarkable achievement that water systems begun more than a century ago for optimum populations of perhaps a hundred thousand have been amplified for huge urban agglomerations. Availability of ready water also contributed to the more measured development of sewerage services, significant parts of it in difficult terrain such as the northern suburbs of Sydney. Perth has been the principal exception to sustained expansion of sewerage, with a significant backlog remaining and substantial residual commitments to septic systems. Coordination of drainage services with water and sewerage elements was largely ignored until the vast increase in urban run-off and consequent pollution eventually concentrated the attention of public policy upon it.

III   WSD Technology and Infrastructure

Before looking at the impact of WSD technology on urban development, a brief description of that technology and its expression as infrastructure is necessary. WSD technology intervenes in the natural water cycle in the following ways:

1.   by storing water in large quantities;

2. by treating water to potable (or drinkable) levels. In Australia, potable water has also been used in large quantities for household, commercial and industrial use;

3. by distributing treated water for household, commercial and industrial use;

4. by collecting wastewater from users and disposing of it through wastewater sewerage systems;

5. by collecting stormwater as drainage and disposing of it through trunk drainage sewers.

Once the water leaves the sewerage network — increasingly through ocean outfalls for major Australian cities — the WSD system has done with it and the natural water cycle resumes through evaporation and precipitation.

Each of these five stages has its distinctive technology and infrastructure. These may be summarised briefly as follows:

- **Water storage.** Major storage reservoirs and control systems. With some storage reservoirs, built canals supplement natural input from river flow and precipitation. Supplementing reservoirs in this way usually requires pumping stations.

- **Water potability.** Water treatment and aeration plants.

- **Water distribution.** Trunk and reticulation pipelines; pumping stations; water treatment and aeration plants; local holding reservoirs.

- **Sewerage.** Trunk and disposal pipelines; pumping stations; sewerage farms; sewerage treatment plants; ocean and estuarine outfalls.

- **Drainage.** Trunk mains; local government disposal mains.

Historically, Australia's WSD infrastructure was provided in accordance with standard international practice in building large-scale engineering works, particularly large dams and headworks. These projects were competently executed and Australia has had few major functional problems with its WSD infrastructure, apart from the inevitable consequences of ageing and obsolescence. Over more than a hundred years, an understandable fixation on providing infrastructure was ingrained in WSD authorities reflected mainly in the strength of their engineering departments, workshops and permanent labour forces. Indeed, in many authorities the engineering arm has been stronger in policy influence than the administrative arm. This has produced a development culture reflected in ceaseless planning for more dams and augmentation of distributive networks. While the influence of demand management, largely through pricing mechanisms, has diminished this developmental engineering culture, it is still influential. Engineering departments have invariably been the toughest units in water authorities to *downsize* and planning for augmentation of water supply systems is still based on the large dam thesis, although the horizons for construction have receded due to reduced demand.

Generally, the WSD technology and its expression as infrastructure has not changed fundamentally since substantial metropolitan provision of WSD services began in the late 19th century. This has been partly due to a low investment in research and development (R&D), less than one per cent of turnover, a factor not confined to Australia, as the CSIRO has pointed out:

> A recent editorial in the Journal of American Water Pollution Control Federation suggested that a Rip Van Winkle awakening today after a fifty year slumber would see many new wonders but would immediately recognise an activated sludge sewerage treatment plant. (CSIRO 1991-1992: 3)

This modern Rip Van Winkle would also have little difficulty in identifying processes such as aeration of water, although he might ponder over the addition of fluoride. Nor would Rip be bamboozled by the intricacies of storage dams although the size and nature of the contemporary materials used would probably impress him. A reticulation pipe is as palpably a distribution pipe as it was 50 years ago, although diameter and composition of materials may differ. Membrane technology could cause some bewilderment, although the concepts underlying its application would be clear enough.

In short, the basics of WSD technology as reflected in WSD infrastructure have not changed all that much. This does not mean that materials have not improved, that better construction methods have not emerged, that substantial technological innovations have not brought much better services. Obviously, modern earth-moving equipment is much more economical, effective and expeditious than hundreds of men with shovels and horse-drawn drays. The two-flush toilet is a pronounced improvement on the throne-like wooden water closet. Membrane technology and new piping materials have provided opportunities for greater flexibility than the standard concrete pipes of earlier years. New technology, however, has not brought any significant change in fundamentals of WSD services which are probably immutable.

Furthermore, the long life cycles of much WSD infrastructure causes substantial delays in technology implementation. A major dam may be technologically obsolescent but, short of structural failure, there is no

little/slow discussion of slow moving tech in WSD

ready way of adapting it significantly through technological innovation. Management can be improved immeasurably through technological changes such as computerised manipulation of flows into and from reservoirs. New technology can be incorporated into ancillary functions such as pumping stations. Trunk, reticulation and disposal pipelines can be replaced gradually as they age and crumble. Even so, the major elements of WSD infrastructure have a fundamental inflexibility that defies substantial modification from technological change. The problem has a cyclical effect because as substantial new infrastructure is provided in accordance with technological change, such as the North Head sewerage treatment and ocean outfall disposals off Sydney, it becomes technologically subservient to the constraints of long life, large investment and gradual depreciation.

Thus, technological innovation will play a role in the development and re-vitalisation of Australia's WSD industry, but it will do so only in fits and starts if Australian cities maintain their present configuration of WSD services. This role will be pitched at the micro-level of infrastructure miniaturisation: through pipes of smaller dimension made of new materials; through a proliferation of small water treatment plants, including package plants; through the development of infrastructure suitable for the exploitation of smaller urban catchment areas. It must also be borne in mind that the WSD industry is lagging behind R&D in crucial related areas such as chemical engineering. A greater involvement of the private sector may also facilitate R&D across a wider spectrum of water-related technology, particularly in the wastewater treatment area. This may amount to an incremental revolution, but it is doubtful whether any substantial impact on urban development and form will emerge within 20 years. Almost certainly, it will take rather longer. While a major transformation of any industry through technological breakthroughs can never be ruled out completely, it would be a brave prophet indeed who would make any such prediction about Australia's WSD systems and services in the 1990s. Current projections, therefore, should be based on relatively modest levels of innovatory technological impact from the WSD industry on urban development.

IV   WSD and Institutional Change

If the technology of water supply and disposal is likely to have a relatively limited impact on urban form and development in the immediate future, is there any prospect of change in WSD administration exercising any significant influence? Three broad models may be defined for the administration of WSD services in Australia:

1. the **unitary model** where one overriding administrative agency is largely responsible for WSD and other major components of the water industry (South Australia, Western Australia, Northern Territory and the ACT);

2. the **statutory authority/LGA model** where administration is divided between central statutory authorities and local government authorities (Victoria, NSW and Tasmania);

3. the **LGA model** where administration is primarily the responsibility of local government (Queensland) (Johnston & Rix 1993: 37ff).

Despite diversity in fundamental administrative structure between the States, WSD administration does not differ significantly in its impact on Australia's major cities. Sydney, Melbourne, Brisbane, Adelaide, Perth, Hobart, Canberra and Darwin are largely administered as metropolitan entities in terms of WSD services despite differences in State administrative models. Until recently, Brisbane would have been included in this list. Although WSD services in Queensland are administered by LGAs, the traditional correlation between the Brisbane City Council boundaries and the conventional limits of metropolitan Brisbane meant that the city's WSD services were predominantly the responsibility of a single huge LGA. With the rapid expansion of urban Brisbane into adjoining shires, the primacy of the Brisbane City Council has been diluted although it retains responsibility for the city's substantial core. (As noted earlier, urban drainage in Sydney is divided in responsibility with the Sydney Water Board responsible for trunk drainage and LGAs managing urban drainage.)

Given this substantial administrative uniformity, it is unrealistic to conclude that WSD administration has had any substantial influence on urban development and form. The choices of WSD administrators have been very much predetermined by historical factors, particularly the technology available to the great public works authorities which built the infrastructure and largely selected the catchments for water storage and the outlets for disposal of wastewater. The administrative cultures of subsequent WSD authorities largely built on or adapted the choices of earlier generations of engineers and administrators.

Nor has the continuing institutional change in WSD authorities since the early 1980s contributed substantively to the impact of WSD on urban development. Certainly, this administrative reform swept away much of the organisational culture and administrative practice shaped by the great developmental era of the 1950s and 1960s. Improved technology also contributed to changes in work practices such as multi-skilling and extended retraining. The reflection of a private sector ethos brought corporatisation to a few larger WSD institutions, the commercialisation of many more, and the contracting-out of traditional functions. Important as were these changes they did not ramify through the technological and infrastructure factors of the WSD structure. These changes had undeniable implications for urban incomes and living patterns but not for familiar configurations of urban form and development.

There is one important component of this seachange in WSD administration, however, that does have important implications for future urban growth. This is the substantial reform of water charging policies which has been implemented in varying degrees in WSD authorities since the early 1980s. The effect of changes in water tariffs to reflect quantities of water actually used as well as fixed charges has considerable potential to reduce demand for water. Already, WSD authorities such as Hunter Water in New South Wales have been able to defer the construction of new storage dams and related infrastructure because higher user charges have constrained water usage. It is too early to speculate that the reliance on distant catchments may have ended because much future planning for urban water storage still hinges on exploitation of even more distant catchments. Already, the water supply of metropolitan Sydney draws from the Shoalhaven River well to the south. For future requirements, there are plans to exploit the headwaters of the Shoalhaven at Welcome Reef which is much closer to urban Canberra than to Sydney. The historical reliance on exploiting ever more distant catchment areas by massive engineering projects is still the norm of many WSD authorities, although the engineering ethos is under increasing challenge from managers impressed by signs of falling demand due to pricing reforms.

In conjunction with reduced demand, a reliance on distant catchment philosophies can also be modified by more effective exploitation of existing catchments. The decision announced by the New South Wales State Government early in 1994 to raise the height of the Warragamba Dam walls was presented essentially as a flood mitigation measure for the Nepean-Hawkesbury River system. Obviously, more water will be stored, providing a means for getting more out of the existing infrastructure and, perhaps, pushing the plans for new dams further into the future. While expedients such as raising the height of storage walls are made more feasible by technological improvement, in no sense are they attributable to technological innovation.

Furthermore, the current fixation of WSD authorities on asset management is directed essentially to locating and listing the existing infrastructure so that its condition can be assessed and it can be made to work effectively. Asset management is also crucial for planning the eventual replacement of WSD infrastructure as it becomes necessary. Although this replenishment and replacement of infrastructure will also reflect technological improvement, it is largely based on incremental refurbishing of traditional WSD supply and disposal systems.

Would substantial corporatisation, even privatisation, change this forecast? An argument could be made that private ownership and enhanced entrepreneurialism in the WSD industry would unleash creative vitality, free more resources for R&D and, ultimately, generate new investment in technological innovation and application. Such arguments ignore the rather indifferent performance of Australian R&D generally and of the private sector particularly. This may be starting to change, but it is worth noting that innovative applications devised by water technology firms such as Memtec largely originated in research programs supported by public sector programs. The privatised English water supply authorities have yet to generate significant investment in research, development and implementation of innovatory technology. (NB This assessment was written before the South Australian Government announced proposals to privatise water supply services. Whatever else the implications of this decision, it is unlikely that it will be influenced in any significant degree by technological innovation. Accordingly its ramifications have not been explored here.)

V   Local Systems — A Retrospective Hypothesis

In the context of Australian urban development the *distant catchment* philosophy was probably inevitable. Was there ever an alternative? A crude hypothetical option can be built on the urbanisation of Sydney in the context of its water supplies. Assume that once the catchment of the Tank Stream had approached its optimum level of supply in the early 19th century, the colonial governor decided to establish a new suburb with a separate water supply system on the closest catchment. The necessary storage and distributive infrastructure for the new suburb was built before settlement began. Urbanisation proceeded on the basis of an urban catchment for each suburb or cluster of suburbs. Urban units emerged on the basis of largely autonomous water services. A localised framework of independent water services was administered by local government units funded by local municipal charges. These water supply systems were administered jointly with municipal drainage services, with human and trade wastes burnt and the residue sold to augment municipal funds.

If a colonial governor ever had the forethought to conceive such a system of incremental urbanisation based on autonomous water supplies, the product would certainly have been a smaller, more compact, less polluted city. Its urban form would have been different with localised water systems built on local catchments preserving natural creek and drainage systems. Much more of the natural vegetation would have survived, improving the aesthetics of urban development by natural barriers between each suburb and catchment area. It would have been easier to plan and build communication corridors.

An obvious drawback to such an hypothesis is the reliance on a uniform spread of smaller catchments through the site of a major city. The old principle of military camouflage that nature never organises anything with maximum uniformity and regularity is applicable here. The irregularity of rivers and creeks draining small catchment areas would have produced a dispersed urbanisation with development thickly concentrated at some points and relatively sparse at others. Such a model may seem idiosyncratic by conventional urban configurations but, crucially, it would have been viable in WSD terms. Furthermore, it would make the contemporary penchant for total catchment planning and management more realistic concepts in terms of their impact on urban planning and development.

While such a vision smacks of Utopianism, it is worth keeping in mind as we look at the impact of WSD provision on urban development and form. Despite its crudeness, it should not be dismissed as futile. A synthesis of contemporary micro-technology together with recent developments in the planning of new urban growth would probably produce something not dissimilar.

VI WSD and Urban Growth

While there are important differences in practice and emphasis, the WSD regimes of the major urban growth areas have much in common. Some divergence has occurred because of topographical differences. For example, the supply and disposal problems of the Swan coastal plain, comprising a large part of metropolitan Perth, differs significantly from metropolitan Sydney, traditionally contained within the coastal basin of the Nepean, Hawkesbury and Georges Rivers. Because the sandy plains of Perth were considered as highly suitable for septic tank sewage disposal, as we have seen, there is a current sewerage backlog of about

30 per cent in Perth. By contrast, Sydney faces intransigent problems with a sewerage system overwhelmingly directed to ocean disposal.

Sydney, Melbourne and Brisbane have some similarities in the reliance on distant catchment areas for the bulk of water supply. Despite the element of distance, these catchments were also those most convenient for large-scale water supply based on storage dams. This convenience factor has to be considered as a qualification of the distant catchment thesis. By comparison, Adelaide has overlooked this convenience factor by not fully exploiting the adjacent catchment of the Adelaide Hills and drawing much of its water supply by pipeline from the Murray River. With the existence of a substantial corridor of flat land to the northwest of the city, Melbourne has been able to exercise a sewerage farm option for a significant part of its disposal, although this option is receding in importance. Overwhelmingly, major Australian urbanisation including Melbourne, will look to the oceans for sewerage disposal.

Other differences have been caused by variations in the timing and pace of urban development. Generally, the strength of urban development has been determined by the longevity of the major cities coupled with the impact of significant commodity, financial and immigration booms. The principal surges of urban development have occurred in Sydney, Melbourne and, in recent years, Brisbane and southeast Queensland. The smaller cities have had sharp spurts of growth, as in Perth at the height of migration after the Second World War, but they have generally grown less rapidly. Canberra and Darwin are essentially administrative cities whose growth has been dictated in large measure by government necessity, although both now show signs of autonomous development from cultural, tourism and regional development. From the perspective of the mid-1990s, it seems that Brisbane, Sydney and, less dramatically, Perth will be the principal areas of sustained growth over the next decade, with Melbourne, Adelaide, and Hobart either growing fitfully or even relinquishing growth. Broad demographic and economic growth patterns will influence the demand for water and consequent pressures for either amplifying current WSD systems or restructuring them.

VII WSD and Urban Form

It is a truism that organised urban existence is wholly dependent on access to potable water supplies. The location of such sources and their exploitation over time is the generative force of all urban civilisation. The absence of a convenient water catchment close to settlement is not an impediment to substantial urban development, as shown by the example of Los Angeles which draws the bulk of its water supply by pipeline from the distant Colorado River. A closer catchment might have produced a more concentrated urban form for Adelaide than the present dispersed metropolis, but not inevitably. The point is that there was no more convenient catchment than the distant Murray River for a city the size of Adelaide. Even if a more convenient catchment had been found for Adelaide, would the development and configuration of the city have been any different? The probability is that Adelaide would still have sprawled up and down the coastal plains much as it does now. Perth, which opted for convenient catchments in the ranges overlooking the coastal plains, has followed a broadly similar pattern of urban development. Whether or not the catchment chosen is the most convenient seems to have little effect on ultimate urban development and form. The crucial factor is the initial technology as embodied in the WSD infrastructure. Whether it is a major storage dam, a series of storage dams, or a pipeline from a river the ultimate impact is similar.

This does not mean, however, that the location of the catchment does not have subsidiary effects on urban development, and these can be quite important. With Sydney, Melbourne and Brisbane the selection of distant but most convenient catchments has been an important influence on direction of urban development, if not the ultimate configuration of the city. The location of principal water sources south of Sydney has helped push the city further to the southwest. The increasing importance of the Shoalhaven catchments south of the historic Nepean dams has also contributed to this urban development of Sydney along a southwest corridor, and not directly south along the axis of the Southern Highlands. Furthermore, the opening up of the Shoalhaven catchment has facilitated urban development in the coastal Illawarra region, quarantined from metropolitan Sydney by the historical catchment areas and the Royal National Park. The Warragamba Dam catchment area has been an important constraint on development to the west. Thus amplification of WSD technology and infrastructure utilising interlocking catchments which have proved to be surprisingly durable and flexible has underpinned Sydney's substantial development towards the Blue Mountains escarpment and along the southwest corridor.

Early choices of catchments, technology and infrastructure have also had an important impact on turning Melbourne's development away from the ranges to the north and northeast where the main storage reservoirs are located. Consequently, the major urban development post-Second World War moved along corridors to the east, southeast, west and, in later years, the northwest. (The Werribee sewerage farm on

Port Phillip Bay to the southwest was an impediment to urban development around the fringes of the bay to the southwest.) Encroachment on catchment areas, diversion around catchment areas, and leapfrogging of catchment areas has been much less emphatic than in Greater Sydney. In recent years, however, planning of cautious urban development has edged closer to the traditional catchments, notably into the Plenty River Valley south of the venerable Yan Yean Reservoir. With Brisbane, the siting of the original city some miles up a navigable river has been the principal force in directing urban development to the coast, and gradual movement towards the catchments has been much less pronounced than in Sydney or Melbourne. With Perth, the urban penetration of the Darling Ranges has undoubtedly been curbed by the existence of principal water sources in the ranges. Consequently, the urban form of Perth owes more to sprawling coastal plain development than the hill-station quality it might have had if different water sources had been chosen or were available.

VIII WSD and Urban Realism

Apart from exercising a strong pull on urban development, WSD technology and infrastructure have exerted an even more decisive influence on the form and appearance of Australia's cities. This effect has been encapsulated neatly in the concept of the *urban carpet* which was increasingly spread over the developing suburbia in the post-war years. Essentially, this involved the destruction of much of the traditional vegetation and its replacement by a neutered environment reflecting European ideals of urban beauty. It has been a regime based on ruthless drainage, a terrain deficient in moisture, luxuriant lawns, and turf monoculture for leisure and recreational areas (football, cricket and hockey fields, racecourses, municipal parks). This stringent modification of natural systems has been rooted in the ready availability of cheap water. Mouritz has described the impact of the imposition of the *urban carpet* regime as a cultural norm on the urban development of Perth:

> Low lying land was either drained to the river and ocean outfalls or filled with the growing waste of the urban community. Streams and rivers were dammed on the adjacent escarpment and the water piped to reservoirs and storage tanks throughout the metropolitan region. The deep sandy soils provided what was believed to be ideal conditions for septic tank sewerage disposal and as a consequence a reticulated system linked to primary treatment came late to the State and even today 30 percent of Perth's households still rely on septics. Much of the indigenous flora was

> quickly and easily removed to be replaced by verdant landscapes supported [by] a cheap and plentiful water supply...These characteristics of suburban development have been ingrained into the lifestyle and culture of Perth's residents and this argument is often used as a reason for the maintenance of the status quo. (1993: 3-5)

With increasing affluence an alternative to the urban carpet has emerged — urban paving or tarmac. This supplements the already extensive urban paving provided by municipal authorities since the middle of the 19th century with tarmac related to urban development processes and the lifestyle fads of individual householders. Some favoured forms of architecture, such as Spanish-style villas, are associated with extensive paving, particularly up-market paving. Conventional urban consolidation projects and smaller commercial developments have encouraged parking tarmac at the expense of both natural vegetation and the urban carpet. Indeed many urban consolidation projects occupy virtually the whole of the available site, eliminating the absorptive effects of traditional urban lawns and vegetation. There is also the ubiquitous, often extensive car park associated with urban shopping centres. Although the urban carpet is reliant on cheap and abundant water, even at its most unaesthetic and wasteful it absorbs urban water run-off. Urban tarmac, on the other hand, is a superb catchment for capturing run-off and discharging it pell-mell to overloaded drainage and sewerage systems.

Australian cities, with their traditional commitment to both the urban carpet and increasing levels of urban tarmac, provide the worst possible amalgam for WSD services. Urban carpet depends on a continuous supply of cheap and plenteous water, a supply that can no longer be guaranteed because of reformist water pricing policies. On the other hand, urban tarmac reduces the direct demand for water supply at the substantial cost of overloading the sewerage and drainage factors of the WSD equation. In combination, they threaten the whole balance of WSD services as they have traditionally existed.

IX   Urban Idealism?

Is there any alternative to the command, even tyranny, that conventional models of WSD provision have asserted over the urban form and urban aesthetics of our cities? The most elaborate proposals have come from the joint perspectives of environmentalism and public policy, as in this vision of a transformed urban water regime:

> In a 'water friendly' urban development, natural hydrological features would be retained. Local drainage and water systems would be integrated

with parks, urban forests and artificial wetlands. Water conservation and recycling technology, built into housing and local facilities, would reduce water inputs and outputs. Design features would include high points for parks, views, ponds and water storage; lowlands for streams, wetlands and lakes; subdivisions and roadways strictly in harmony with natural topography. Costs usually associated with major infrastructure such as extensions to trunk sewers and stormwater drains would be minimised by using local scale systems. . . Original springs, streams and wetlands would be retained, becoming desirable aesthetic and functional features of the plan. . . Stormwater would be collected from roofs and stored on site in water tanks. Greywater would be recycled into gardens. Access run-off would be channelled into interconnected nature strips and swales running along contour lines and draining into natural streams and wetlands and recreational lakes. Water would be drawn from streams and lakes to irrigate urban forests and parks and domestic and market gardens. (Johnston & Rix 1993: 261)

Is this a phantasmagoria, a pipe dream? Although complex in public policy, planning and administrative terms, its technological implications are modest and achievable. It would require localised water treatment plants to deliver drinking water of a high quality. Package programs for sewerage treatment would be essential but costs would be offset to some degree with by-products such as methane gas. Storage and reticulation systems could take advantage of smaller diameter pipelines, flexible new materials for piping systems and membrane retention technology. Other low level technology could be incorporated into the system without excessive cost, such as small hydro-electric units or water wheels to power low wattage pumps during storms to fill underground storage tanks at high points in the landscape. Overall, expenditure on new technology and incorporating it into localised WSD systems would be relatively low compared with the costs of enhancing, maintaining and replacing the traditional systems and their infrastructure. For example, conventional local government drainage systems provided by concrete kerbing and guttering alongside established roadways could be replaced by sloping grass swales.

The relative modesty of new investment in localised systems would be offset, perhaps overwhelmed, by the changes in public mind-set, conventional WSD practices and government procedures needed to make such a transformation work. Even more daunting would be the implications of writing off the huge historical investment in traditional WSD assets, particularly storage dams, distribution mains, and wastewater disposal systems.

X   The New Utopia?

Even five years ago a proposal on the model outlined above would have been regarded as hopelessly irresponsible, as smacking of Schumacher and the *small is beautiful* movement. Indeed, it has much similarity with the crude model of how cities such as Sydney might have developed by leapfrogging from catchment to catchment (see above). There is evidence, however, that localised WSD delivery is being taken with increasing seriousness by developers and planners. Here are three examples.

The Rouse Hill project in Sydney's northwest sector was approved by the New South Wales State Government in 1989 as a joint exercise involving the Sydney Water Board and private sector development. The Rouse Hill Infrastructure Consortium has been formed to fund and project-manage water, sewerage and drainage functions for part of the Rouse Hill Development Area which is one of three substantial urban developments projected to absorb part of the city's metropolitan growth into the 21st century. The deed of agreement between the Board and the Consortium stipulates the use of innovative planning and infrastructure technology. Rouse Hill is one of several sites trialing distributed treatment strategy for wastewater. (Others include the Plenty Valley Corridor in Melbourne and the development site for the Multi-function Polis in Adelaide.) The objectives of distributed treatment strategy have been described thus:

> Instead of a high-import, high-flow, high-export system, the strategy is to reduce the imports and exports of water from urban sub-regions per unit time, by devoting fewer resources to piping systems, and increasing the level of local treatment and local routing of effluent and by-products. When this treatment strategy is also combined with re-use, additional aspects have to be incorporated such as heightening public awareness of water conservation and pollution control behaviours, increasing differentiation of water resources by their product quality, integration with land planning (eg open space irrigation) and possibly bioremediation for say, heavy metals or pathogens. (Sydney Water Board 1991-1992: 113)

Using water reclamation and reuse strategies and technologies locally administered is a viable alternative to centralised WSD services but Australian cities have only begun to nibble at the edges.

The Rouse Hill development is very much an example of how localised, autonomous WSD systems might be introduced in urban fringe development. The concept of Water Sensitive Design tries to manage existing catchments in line with emerging technology and design criteria to develop localised WSD system and practices. Mouritz, who has been closely associated with the development of the concept, perceives it as building on government initiatives in developing Integrated Catchment Management:

> The opportunity for total water cycle management approaches, small scale technologies, reuse systems and their link to urban planning and design are presently being investigated. Ultimately, it is envisioned that these approaches will lead to identifying opportunities for the productive use of stormwater and wastewater resources and consequently more sustainable urban futures. (Mouritz 1992: 1)

Perth has been the principal city in the development of the Water Sensitive Design concept through a sequence of land and water research studies and policy initiatives undertaken during the 1980s and into the 1990s. These were largely spurred by a loss of wetland environments in metropolitan Perth, estimated at up to 80 per cent, coupled with an adherence to the urban carpet approach to water use "ingrained into the lifestyle and culture of Perth residents" (Mouritz 1992: 4). Hypothetical studies of development utilising Water Sensitive Design were conducted, taking account of existing wetlands and regional groundwater patterns, and a planning framework has been proposed to link water resource management with land planning and urban development in a more structured and coordinated way. Perth's largest urban drainage catchment, the Bayswater Drain, has been used as the basis for studying more closely the implications of Water Sensitive Design for local government planning schemes in a context of urban consolidation and renewal:

> Our aim is to identify a picture of new urban land and water futures which, although they might seem unrealistic in the short-term, are desirable targets to aim for. Underlining this work is the concept of 'total water cycle management', a commitment to evaluate the potential or more localised water, smaller scale technologies and a belief that the constant flux of nutrients and contaminants being transferred from land to natural water systems is not sustainable. For the sake of nutrient conservation these cycles must be closed and the production of useful biomass from stormwater and wastewater resources must be a minimum target. Similarly the non-degradable toxic substances in these fluxes must be prevented from entering food chains. . . The concept [of Water Sensitive Design] has been based on the belief that the integration of land and water planning could lead to better land allocation decisions and development of an urban form and character more sympathetic to the local landscape. (Mouritz 1992: 13-4)

Conceptually, the Water Sensitive Design process is a venture into total urban water cycle management similar in basic respects to the Rouse Hill development. Both are attempts to achieve urban integrated catchment management. The salient difference is that Rouse Hill is a new urban development on the metropolitan fringe; Water Sensitive Design is an attempt to renew and better manage an extensive urban drainage catchment in an existing highly urbanised area of a substantial Australian city.

A hypothetical exercise conducted by Clark and Desmier in Adelaide indicated that a replicated, small-scale *cascading* approach to providing WSD and floor mitigation services was technologically and hydrologically feasible in the urbanised Adelaide plains and contiguous hills. Essentially, this involved the *cascading* of run-off, treated effluent and recharged groundwater from the hills to lower urban areas. According to the authors, the annual cost of localised systems based on the *cascading* principle would be much the same as the centralised metropolitan system drawn largely from the distant Murray River. While the opportunity for building of major storage dams in the Adelaide hills had long passed, the catchment potential of the hills could be used to feed localised, integrated WSD systems on the urbanised foothills and plains below.

XI WSD, Technology and Urban Consolidation

How realistic are opportunities for significant reorganisation of Australia's cities from centralised WSD systems traditionally based on distant catchments into small-scale, decentralised systems based on contemporary micro-technology? Much depends on concentration of urban population. It is clearly easier to evolve such integrated local systems in new urbanisation on the metropolitan fringe, such as the Rouse Hill development in Sydney. Yet the current policy focus is against the continuation of metropolitan growth based on incrementalism at the fringes and towards the more intensive use of conventional infrastructure through urban consolidation.

There is no fundamental technological reason why substantial residential renewal of obsolete industrial space and the intensive consolidation of existing residential areas through replacement of conventional detached and semi-detached housing lots by home units, town houses, and villas should not be based on localised WSD systems. Inner city reservoirs could be created on defunct industrial sites or located underground. (An early plan for Sydney's central water system incorporated a reservoir under Sydney University.) Run-off from urban tarmac and paving could be channelled into such reservoirs, assisting in the alleviation of drainage problems. Mains Interception Sewerage Treatment (MIST) technology could be utilised, perhaps by putting treatment plants on top of trunk sewerage mains, to recycle effluent into a local network. In heavily urbanised areas smaller reclamation and treatment plants could be incorporated into tarmac car parks and tennis courts. The net result would certainly be ample water stocks, perhaps even an over-supply. Local WSD networks of this sort however, would probably be less attractive aesthetically than similar local networks on the urban fringe or even those in suburbs developed on the traditional urban carpet grid of quarter acre blocks. They would be just as viable, perhaps even more so, than local networks developed according to *greener* principles.

These suggestions are highly tentative, not to say speculative. We do not have any clear picture of what a local water catchment and network might look like or how it might operate in a heavily urbanised area. What would be the impact of such an urban configuration on traditional approaches to centralised WSD systems and services? Substantial urban consolidation is often predicated as a means of getting much more intensive usage out of existing urban space, that is, multiplying dwellings and persons per hectare provides a more effective usage of costly infrastructure. With traditional WSD infrastructure, however, the argument is complicated by the nature of the infrastructure and its relative obsolescence. Substantial urban consolidation raises the prospect of bringing more water greater distances for more intensive usage, with consequent additional strains on disposal systems. Furthermore, this would have to be done at periods when long-established traditional infrastructure was urgently in need of replacement and renewal.

It is a reasonable assumption, therefore, that urban consolidation would work better if metropolitan WSD systems could be reorganised on the basis of local urban catchments and networks. Indeed, urban consolidation futures are implicit in the analysis of practitioners like Mouritz (1992) and Clark (1992) who are sympathetic to the doctrine. The overwhelming problem is what to do with the traditional infrastructure. Should it gradually be wound down in consonance with an equally gradual reconfiguration of autonomous urban catchments and networks? Or should it continue in uneasy alliance with emergent local systems, particularly in metropolitan fringe development, with consequent risks of systems duplication and over-supply of water? Even if a consensus emerged to eventually scrap the traditional system and localise WSD services, how could this be coordinated with planning of local government, transport, telecommunications, community and other services? In many respects the availability of suitable technology is the least formidable of the many problems associated with a sustainable re-configuration of urban WSD services.

XII Conclusion

Selection of principal water sources and the exploitation of these sources to provide WSD services has made a major impact on the development and form of Australia's great cities. The overwhelming reliance on distant catchments has influenced the geography of development, particularly in Sydney and Melbourne, the two largest cities. Choices about the spread and direction of urban development in these two great cities have been determined in important ways by the need to protect major catchments from encroachment and pollution. The choice of distant catchments has also largely determined the technology of supplying WSD services. As a result, a uniformity of infrastructure has emerged directed to supplying and disposing of huge volumes of water, in fact guaranteeing water surpluses beyond what is necessary to ensure basic urban growth and household health and welfare. Together with historically cheap tariffs for water, this distinctive mix of infrastructure, largely dictated by technology relevant at the time to exploiting distant catchments, has contributed to the rapid urban development and idiosyncratic sprawl and configuration of Australian cities. Furthermore, availability of abundant cheap water and the ability to dispose of it readily, although not without some pain, has contributed to aesthetic qualities reflecting the urban carpet rather than preservation of original topography and vegetation. Unquestionably, WSD technology has made an incalculable impact on the development, form and aesthetics of our cities. Apart from the accidents of original settlement, it is probably the most important factor in Australian urban growth and form.

Will this ever change? Certainly, the technology exists which would permit the breaking up of monolithic WSD systems servicing whole metropolitan areas and their replacement by smaller systems exploiting local catchments, whether natural or based on artificial cycles of reclamation and recycling. For this to be achieved, a huge infrastructure inertia would have to be overcome with the writing off of entrenched historical systems. It would be a difficult transition although the principal barriers would be cultural and administrative rather than economic. Continued urban development at the metropolitan fringes allows opportunities for replacing centralised WSD systems with regional or local systems based on new technology in water harvesting, reclamation and recycling. Furthermore, this micro-technology is modest in terms of its demands on space and public finance compared with the alternative of incremental expansion and refurbishment of traditional systems. Urban consolidation also provides opportunities for restructuring the systems and there have been some interesting hypothetical studies of how this might be done. It is possible, however, that the impact of processes such as Water Sensitive Design and cascading could be most significant in outer urban areas where major consolidation programs are less likely to emerge. There must be some doubt about whether consolidation of inner-urban sites will provide sufficient impulse for such a re-configuration. Certainly, substantial consolidation projects are now proceeding at inner-urban locations apparently predicated on existing WSD systems. In this combination of circumstances, water pricing policies will probably have a much greater impact than technological innovation on the emergence of new WSD systems and their contribution to future urban development.

Chapter 4

COMMUNICATIONS

Don Lamberton

In *Clear Across Australia* Ann Moyal (1984) has given us a detailed, graphic story of the development of telecommunications in Australia. The telegraph was first introduced in Victoria in 1854. The Overland Telegraph Line across Central Australia brought direct cable communication as from 19 November 1871 with the rest of the world. Her history records these events and traces the long telecommunications revolution up to the mid-1980s: from "the most perfect invention of modern times", as the *Argus* called the electric telegraph in 1853, to the days of satellites and optical fibre. She deals with technical innovation, the people and their skills, decision-making, organisational arrangements and the policies as the number of telephones grew from less than 30,000 at the turn of the century to more than six million when her chronicle ends. Perhaps this diffusion of the new technology was only to be expected, given the tyranny of distance, and was a premonition of Australia's readiness to gorge itself on information technology (IT) in coming decades.

It is commonplace now to speak of the telecommunications system as the central nervous system of the global economy. According to a World Bank perspective this system is:

> [T]he means by which the world's business is conducted, organised and managed. Companies and countries that cannot effectively participate in these systems cannot effectively participate in the global economy. With telecoms becoming ever more important and the speed of progress in the developing world increasing, the gap is widening between the telecom "haves" and the "have nots". There is a serious danger that, unless the developing world can accelerate and reform its telecom development it will be permanently disadvantaged. (Nulty 1992: 4)

This perspective is applied by the Bank to the least developed countries and the middle income or newly industrialising countries but much of the argument is equally applicable to small and developed nations.

It is interesting therefore to find a century-old Australian version of the central nervous system analogy: Melbourne's telephone exchange was described as the "*cerebellum* of the social and commercial system of the busy city ... incessantly receiving and transmitting from and to every portion of the vital organism" (Moyal 1984: 79). And there was recognition of the concept of "service to the bush". Also the distinction between a telecommunications system managed on business lines, as opposed to services-oriented operation, with "a duty to render to those who do not crowd themselves into cities", was raised quite early.

But what does not emerge in this excellent history is the impact of telecommunications on the spatial dimension of the Australian economy; on, for example, the growth of cities. This comment is in no sense a criticism: it was not on Moyal's agenda. Had she chosen to tackle spatial questions, she would have become embroiled in the unravelling of the impact of telecommunications in economic growth and the role cities play in that process.

Much of the debate about this set of spatial issues rests on an *enabling* notion of information technology which fits easily into a broad pattern of thought about communication. As psychologist George Miller wrote a decade ago:

> Communication has become an American obsession. Those who admire it justify the obsession as a necessary precondition for democratic government, or for a free economy; others view it less favourably as a defence against the loneliness of personal independence, or against the insecurity of competitive co-existence. Whatever the reason, the vast communication industries that have sprung up in this century now bathe every willing citizen in a continuous and unprecedented flow of written, spoken, musical, and pictorial messages. The Earl of Chesterfield to the contrary, knowledge of the world can now be acquired in a closet. Social and economic changes that have accompanied this effusion of communication, first in the United States and now worldwide, do clearly signal a New Industrial Revolution. (1983: ix)

This pattern of thought is supported by modelling and futurology that often amounts to little more than linear extrapolation, performed without reflection on Keynes' remark that we use the convention that the future resembles the past because our imagination and our knowledge are too weak to tell us what particular changes to expect (1937: 13).

Another view, at times either an extension of the enabling notion or an alternative, is perhaps inadequately labelled as the control interpretation, although the words do capture an essential element. There must be room for consideration of power, monopoly and exploitation.

In the one case the literature depicts happy workers in electronic cottages in idyllic locations, no doubt with high real incomes in terms of both material and positional goods (Hirsch 1977). In the other, there is isolation and a prospect of a lifetime in front of the flat screen, for education, entertainment, work and daily data needs. As Castells warns:

> Historical optimism and moralistic pessimism both convey in different tones an equally simplistic message of technological determinism, be it in the liberation of the individual from the constraints of the locale, or the alienation of social life disintegrating in the anonymity of suburban sprawl. (1989: 1)

A further contention by Castells needs to be accommodated in our research ventures if we are to penetrate the role of communications in shaping spatial patterns: "Telecommunications is reinforcing the commanding role of major business concentrations around the world" (1989:1-2).

While I am inclined to agree, I must do so on the basis of theory rather than empirical findings, but first I must point to some analytical difficulties:

1. Telecommunications is only part of IT. Despite all the talk about *convergence* of telecommunications and computer technologies, both have fuzzy boundaries, changing in themselves, and diffusing throughout both domestic and international economies. The nature of convergence is never made clear and can contain a host of possibilities. Clearly interaction and integration, in an industrial organisation sense, occurs within and between the relevant industrial units. Nevertheless, it is difficult to deal with the complex interrelationships involved in the software and multimedia developments as simply part of a *convergence* process.

2. The telecommunications system caters for only part of the communication process. Let us try to put aside the fascinating and complex details of copper wires, satellites, fibre, dishes and keyboards to focus on the underlying function: there is a sequence of the symbol-manipulating services, inquiring, communicating, deciding (Marschak 1968). A significant chunk of capital formation goes to the provision of the services, and

must include not only information-handling equipment but also the human skills and organisational capital needed to ensure capability of managing these services and using the output — and that output is information.

Information is transmitted through telecommunications but it is also transmitted in other ways: through the written word and in conversation; it is embodied in goods that are produced and traded; and it is transmitted by the movement of people through travel and migration. The same goes for information storage. We are told about the remarkable storage capacity of disks but not always warned about their obsolescence. However we should not neglect either the storage capacity of the human brain or the role of organisational capital.

3. The core activity is the use of information and we tend to take this for granted. Economics is much at fault in this respect. The most sophisticated of traditional modelling employed an assumption of perfect knowledge, which would seem logically to have denied the existence of a sector of the economy accounting for some two-fifths of employment. The more recent fashion of rational expectations theory is in some respects a return to the earlier assumption: that good use is made of what is apparently a reasonably adequate information base and there is no call to bother about the costs of information and the problems of information management.

This is not the place for detailed consideration of this assumption. However, some of its implications cannot be avoided: for example, "full relevant information for a chooser must include knowledge of what others are choosing" (Shackle 1972: 264). Surely this becomes an important matter for the application of economic theory to the planning process.

Other approaches treat information as a resource, as a commodity, as perception of pattern, as a constitutive force in society (Braman 1989). The interdisciplinary study of information (Machlup & Mansfield 1983) takes in information economics (Lamberton 1971, 1984, 1993a), organisational approaches (Macdonald, 1995), information science, cognitive science, and many other disciplinary efforts. In their various ways these studies seek to clarify the role of information and the capability of using information in economic growth, the formation of organisations and policy, ie, all levels of forms of guidance for action in the face of uncertainty (Shackle 1969).

I   Telecommunications and Economic Development

These considerations go a good deal of the way in explaining the inconclusiveness of the debate about telecommunications and economic development. Some continue to preach that substantial investment in telecommunications equipment is the linchpin in national productivity. However, such superficial reasoning must give way to sophisticated attempts to determine the direction of causality between telecommunications investment and economic growth.

Studies of United States data (Hardy 1980; Cronin et al 1991, 1993) have claimed to show strong relationships between economic activity and telecommunications infrastructure. Increases in output or gross national product (GNP) lead to increases in investment in telecommunications; increases in telecommunications investment stimulate overall economic growth. Hardy's study related to data from 45 countries over 1960-1973. Cronin et al used United States aggregate data for 1958-1988 for their first study and, in their more recent study, data for the State of Pennsylvania and two counties within Pennsylvania. Different measures of telecommunications infrastructure gave similar results, for example per capita telecommunications investment and per capita telephone access lines.

Because these findings and the problems of measurement and interpretation bear directly upon the relationships that might exist at city level, we need to dwell upon them. The tests of *causality* applied were Granger and modified Sims, plus Dickey-Fuller tests. In the absence of a reasoned theoretical account for the existence of a causal relationship that goes beyond correlation and regression, I must confess to some doubts about these findings as the basis for massive investment decisions, especially in countries in which tastes, technology and institutional arrangements differ a good deal from those in the United States. As I do not think we have reached the end of the spurious correlation/spurious regression debate, I should be much happier with a theoretical base that linked the use of information, of various kinds, to the process of growth.

In keeping with this suggestion of a more complex conception of the role of information and information machines in economic development, development can be defined as "a process of system evolution towards more and more complex patterns of coordinated activities". The lowering of transportation costs, by extending markets over space — and incidentally reducing the costs of transmitting information — had been a major force tending to increase the division of labour. "It is reasonable to believe that the costs of processing, transmitting and storing information have by now taken over the role in economic development that transportation costs played for so long" (Leijonhufvud 1989: 165).

Information-intensive production has been fostered by the large business units and governmental agencies as the dominant form of organisation and by changes in production processes (Castells 1989: 18) which have favoured a greater role for science, technology and management. Organisation as well as product and technology had therefore to become a variable (Lamberton 1984). On the consumption side, mass markets combined with collective consumption triggered "a flurry of information-gathering systems and information-distributing flows" (Castells 1989: 18).

Understandably, these trends fuelled thoughts about *global* possibilities, with accompanying profit expectations. The term global has not been given any precise meaning. Holland (1988) is the only theoretical paper to come to my notice which attempts to define global economy and treat it as an adaptive process. At the end of the day, however, the Holland model seems to be the competitive model writ large, although it may pave the way for some aspects of the real world such as hierarchical organisation, communication and changing technologies. In the meantime, I should favour more precision in the use of the term; for the most part, internationalisation suffices (Lamberton 1993a).

While both production and consumption have been affected in the course of these changes, information economy studies have shown that the bulk of the output of information goods and services becomes input to production, rather than being consumed by households (Jonscher 1983; Lamberton 1993b). Firms and government acquire these information goods and services. On this, the historical account is incomplete but Moyal tells us that:

> City business operations, long dependent on cables and telegrams, were speeded by telephone service. There were other clients. Fire brigades, police stations, hospitals, were among the earliest connections. Leading doctors took out subscriptions. . . Banks, solicitors, insurance companies, auctioneers, printers, importers, brokers, merchants and the press made early use of the striking new facility. (1984: 78)

If we wish to focus on the role of information in order to achieve a different perspective on cities, we must look finally to the special economic characteristics of information. First and foremost, we must note that "even though information can be a commodity, it is one only to a limited extent" (Arrow 1984: 142). Because information is indivisible and difficult to appropriate, we cannot simply treat it as just another one of the commodities in market models. With regard to indivisibility:

> [I]nformation about a method of production, for example, is the same regardless of the scale of the output. Since the cost of information depends only on the item, not its use, it pays a large-scale producer to acquire better information than a small-scale producer. Thus, information creates economies of scale throughout the economy, and therefore, according to well-known principles, causes a departure from the competitive economy. (Arrow 1984: 142)

So the fundamental characteristics of information link with the dominant forms of organisation.

These considerations lead me to suggest that we need a history of a different kind if we are to understand the role of information and ask questions about the knowledge-based city as various authors are now doing (eg Knight 1993). It would need an input/output-style modelling of information flows; it would focus on the forms of organisation; and it just might enable us to explain why information activities that would seem potentially footloose, still tend to be concentrated in cities. I may misjudge the current literature but it is my impression that the informational city of such authors as Castells, Moss and Hepworth, is more a technological than an informational phenomenon.

An explanation of the reinforcing effects that Castells reports needs to combine labour intensity and propinquity. This circumstance can arise from various sources: for example, production conditions, communication processes, management control, and labour preferences. In the present context I wish to emphasise a neglected aspect associated with the characteristics of information and the communication process.

A number of dichotomies have been introduced in attempts to understand the decision process: for example, objective versus subjective, routine versus creative, optimisation versus innovation, training versus education, data versus voice. Each tends to link with human participation. A further distinction between codifiable information and tacit knowledge as argued by Nelson (1980, 1981), not only links with labour intensity but requires the presence of labour in an organisational context if communication is to be effective and learning is to take place. Irrespective of the source to which we wish to attribute this outcome — production, communication, control or preferences, there are clear spatial implications.[1]

---

1   I am indebted to PhD student, John Trent for a strengthened appreciation of this line of argument.

II   The City and its Technologies

Technology is embodied in and interwoven with the architecture of cities, the equipment in the homes, offices, factories and transportation systems, and the minds and skills of workers, managers and residents. Thriving or obsolete, the relationship of cities with each other and with the world around them has both complementary and competitive elements that are outcomes of old, new and future technologies.

Any attempt to obtain a snapshot of the technologies of Australian cities is plagued by lack of official statistics so we turn to the research publication of the relatively few active researchers studying this aspect of technological change. Newton argues that:

> Telecommunications represents the new urban infrastructure. What water, road and rail have represented as primary networks to previous economic eras, telecommunications now represents to the information economy of advanced societies. Telecommunications is the primary vehicle for information exchange that precedes, or accompanies, virtually all economic transactions: banking (automatic teller machines), shopping (electronic funds transfer-point of sale), ordering goods (electronic data exchange), messaging, facsimile, electronic-mail. (1991: 54)

Newton attributes the perceived increasing importance of telecommunications to two trends: "the emergence of societies that are information and knowledge-based, and the emergence of a global economy" (1991: 54).

When the information sector was defined (Newton 1991, 1993) as communications, finance, property, business, etc, public administration, community services, its share of employment nationally rose from 17 per cent to 36 per cent between 1954 and 1986. Of the State capitals only Adelaide exceeded this rate of change, as did Newcastle, Wollongong, Geelong, Townsville, Ballarat and Cairns. We can follow Newton's account of the changing pattern in terms of international telephone traffic, distribution of 008 subscribers, penetration of facsimile, cellular mobile telephone subscribers, high-speed data lines, and the emerging fibre optic network. I have doubts, however, about what we can glean from such analysis.

First, there is the role of *technology push*, technological innovation always being a mixture of the push element along with demand pull. This does seem to be important in the case of telecommunications and for IT generally. I can give no better illustration than the Geneva 1991 World Telecommunications Exhibition and Forum, the latest in a 20-year series reflecting the growth of the telecommunications industry. It was judged by the organisers to have been very successful, the criteria being the total amount spent (more than A$0.75 billion), the presence of 1000 stars of the industry (ministers and CEOs), and the conduct of business at a dizzying pace. But even the *Telecom 91 Daily* could see a downside: the neglect of the needs of developing countries, the absence of a clear theme and the technical pornography. This major event had as its slogan, "An interconnected world: improving the quality of life for all".

In other settings, even less in the way of constraints on imagination are admitted. The experts who envisage the cyberspace world of "vast data bases that constitute the culture's deposited wealth" where "every document is available, every recording is playable, and every picture is viewable" (Benedikt 1991: 2), nevertheless find room for sweatshops in their "harsh, nightmarish . . . man-made information jungle".

It should therefore be no surprise that United States corporations gorged themselves on IT. Information processing equipment as a percentage of all durable equipment bought by private enterprise (excluding farms) increased from 11 per cent in 1970 to 51 per cent in 1989 (*The Economist* 1991: 30). If comparable statistics were available, the Australian story might well be similar. In neither country is there strong reason to think that the rate of return on this investment has been high. In fact it is a common allegation that this investment has not been a paying proposition.

A second consideration generating doubt is that there are no statistics of capacity utilisation even at the national level, let alone for cities. New technologies are never well-catered for by the statistical establishments and when the impact is as pervasive as it seems to be with IT, this lack of information is a serious matter for both research and policy. Even the OECD, which has taken a keen interest in IT developments and devoted resources to data collection, has failed to seek not only measures of utilisation of IT capital but also indicators of the use of information.

Closely related to this, inadequate attention has been given to the complementary resources that are needed if IT is to be used effectively in information processes. We do well to recall Schumpeter's remark about the stock of capital:

> [It] is neither homogeneous nor an amorphous heap. Its various parts complement each other in a way that we readily understand as soon as we hear of buildings, equipment, raw materials and consumers' goods. Some of these parts must be available before we can operate others; and various sequences or lags between economic actions impose themselves and further restrict our choices; and they do this in ways that differ greatly according to the composition of the stock we have to work on. (1953: 631)

The linchpin approach tends to neglect the complementarities, the sequences or lags. In a modern economy, information activities (creation, handling, storage, manipulation and use), taken together, are the dominant call on resources. This applies to both the manufacturing and service sectors. As mentioned earlier, in a two-sector model the bulk of information goods and services are used by manufacturing and government.

These producer services play a crucial role in determining overall productivity. Because of the complexity and pervasiveness of IT, it becomes a major management task to ensure that both optimisation and innovation proceeds effectively and that the infrastructure is informationally efficient.

The rationale for information infrastructure and services that has been most frequently put forward is that information is an essential resource for good management, productivity gains, competitiveness and development generally. The mere presence of IT, even expenditure on IT, has been taken as proof enough of the beneficial use of information. The great gap in analyses, for management, policy and research purposes, has been and remains the use of information and its impact on business and governmental activity. Menou points to the growth of information services and the "serious questioning" that has arisen from all sides regarding their "relevance, appropriateness and sustainability" (1993: 2). He reports that the fuzziness of the key concepts led the Information Sciences and Systems Division of the Canadian International Development Research Centre (IDRC) to initiate a major project which is seeking to, first, clarify the process by which information use is turned into, and perceived as, a lasting benefit by the various stakeholders; and, second, to identify and develop meaningful indicators, both qualitative and quantitative, by which the benefits of information can be assessed.

Until such assessment can be carried out, technology push will tend to dominate. We need, therefore, to give much more attention to information capabilities and organisational capital. These are matters that involve people and I think it significant that in so many of the information systems management texts people get a passing reference as decision-makers in Chapter 1 and reappear as problem constraints in the final chapter.

In drawing attention to these constraints, we meet frequent mention of information overload. While individual capabilities are extended by the new technologies, those capabilities nevertheless remain limited. This is why there is recourse to organisational forms that seek a trade-off between economies in information gathering and the costs of disseminating information to those members of the organisation thought best able to put it to use.

The overload discussion has a long history, and proposed solutions, mostly of a technological character, seek to compress the decision-maker's essential information into one page or ensure that *all* relevant information is brought to bear in the decision process. For the most part this discussion misses the point that the organisational form is a variable. Changing patterns of labour specialisation have been characteristic of the entire process of economic development and this holds for the recent informatisation. New specialisations with new job labels have been emerging in what can now be seen as the industrialisation of information activities; in monitoring, gathering, processing, computation, storing, transmission and decision.

Some argue that the solution to the problems of both theory and practice lie in treating information as a commodity. However, for reasons relating to divisibility and appropriability, information is a commodity only to a limited extent. As a consequence, much activity is directed to the provision of information services and the exercising of control over access to and use of information (Boyle 1992). This does not invalidate the conceptual approach that treats information as one form of capital and the capability of using information, ie, organisation, as another complementary form of capital. Nor does it invalidate productivity thinking, which does no more than pose the question whether one way of achieving an objective is more advantageous than another.

The greatest danger, from a management perspective, is that the productivity gains are assumed to ensure competitiveness. In a climate of technology hype it is easy to overlook the competitive nature of the use of IT. Methods that can be adopted easily by all competitors do not confer advantage. However, the experience to date with IT and changing forms of organisation suggest that there may be scope for organisational innovation. The case of management information systems (MIS) can serve as an illustration. The thrust of application of the computer for many years was to provide more of the old kinds of information rather than use the new capability in data analysis. Those who saw beyond the hype and innovated in this way secured advantage.

The emergence of the global economy was the other trend said to have brought increasing importance to telecommunications. There are a few qualifications that need to be added:

1. Global village thinking seems to come easily to all those involved in marketing telephones. This was the perspective when the International Telecommunications Union provided the

statistic that: "over half the world's population is not yet within two hours walking distance of a telephone" (Butler 1988: 1). Of course the implications of this asymmetry are vastly different if one has an equity perspective.

2.   Regionalisation, with major cities as the contact points, appears to be a better description of world market evolution than globalisation, whatever meaning this term is given (Lamberton 1993a). Information, communication and coordination aspects dominate in this integration process. If we treat the information resource as shorthand for the information stocks and flows, the capability of managing that resource, and the institutions that have been created for that management, I believe there is reason to think, first, that an existing distribution of information resources may confer a comparative advantage on a regional bloc; and, second, that regional blocs may achieve further advantage through specialisation in information activities.

3.   As a final comment on the global outlook, we might ask where are the global firms. Only a short time ago, the response would have been to name IBM, but IBM's experience is leading to a transformation. Finance and advertising firms also have encountered barriers. As *The Economist* remarked:

> Financial markets may indeed have turned global, but that does not mean that every financial intermediary must build a costly worldwide network. The business and the variables that determine comparative advantage are more complicated than that.(1990: 16)

The changing pattern is one in which functions are being rearranged, some being decentralised while others are centralised. Some see the pattern of incentives and costs favouring: "Production ... becoming more local and regional; trade ... becoming more continental; and capital and currency markets ... becoming more international" (Daniel Bell cited in Swedberg 1990: 229).

So perhaps the supporting influence on telecommunications is just more of old-fashioned internationalisation in a rather dynamic world society.

III   Infrastructure

Cities are a major part of a nation's capital: there are the equipment and buildings of mainstream economics but there are also the human capital, organisational capital and information capital that make cities places of education, market places of ideas, sources of innovation, and generators of technology. They are at once communication and coordination networks, transportation systems and information industries.

Their complexity calls into question the tendency, in both urban and industrial policy discussions, to lump all kinds of capital together as infrastructure. Perhaps the most common practice is an even less desirable one — to include only physical assets and think only in terms of hardware technology.

Such preoccupation with technology can have dangerous consequences. As David and Steinmueller say in respect to computer technology, it is a major problem:

> [W]hen becoming fixated upon some vision of a distant technological utopia leads many constituent elements of the existing . . . information system to be viewed as merely a collection of unforseen road-blocks, extraneous binding constraints that can now be identified as requiring removal if the computer revolution is to proceed. (1991: 39)

Of course, the features holding up the show turn out to be deeply embedded and difficult to change. They note:

> [T]he way children are taught from kindergarten onward, the mathematical literacy of our population, the role defined for university teachers, the present arrangement for the protection of intellectual property rights, the power of established disciplines entrenched within departmental fortifications. (1991: 39)

In the *New York Times* we could read that infrastructure still evokes 1930s images of big public works that helped bring industrial prosperity but it is "largely a symbol, a metaphor capable of generating some pretty fancy daydreams" (Muschamp 1993: 32): architects see opportunity to move their profession toward social service; it suggests access to large chunks of public money; and it holds promise of linking buildings, neighbourhoods and regions.

The infrastructure initiative permits a major technology push for the new IT and distracts attention from the need for evaluation of the substantial investment outlays that are involved.

The outlays relate to a diverse set of activities: for example network formation, electronic highways, smart buildings, information utilities, home shopping facilities, and distance education. Evaluation must look to both technology and the organising for management of technology. Those who ask whether cities are to be bypassed with the creation of superhighways for talk and data need to know whether the existing telecommunications services have dispersed activity or simply reinforced the commanding role of business and governmental concentrations. Those who favour inner-city residential development need to look back to the impact of technological change on the provision of services while those opposed to such development might ponder how societies would preserve their identity and cohesiveness.

IV Conclusion

The central point is that cities, whatever else they might be, are communication centres. The evidence is not to be found in the presence of information machines but in the stocks and flows of information. These are the indicators of the information or knowledge-based city. And here I must acknowledge my indebtedness to Richard Meier (1960, 1962, 1980) whose pioneering work on a communications theory of urban growth dates back to 1960. I hope I have been able to add just a little to his ideas by fusing them with developments in information economics.

If we persist with the economist's production function-type analysis, we have to include information and the capability of using information amongst the inputs and reckon information as output. The cost of information must be made explicit. We must take account of the economic characteristics of information and organisation.

I note a recent comment that "While the economics of information has transformed academic economics, it has had a less systematic effect on policy making" (Morduch 1993: 931). To say this may be to overstate the achievement but I contend that analysis that ignores information as resource and output, of economies or cities within those economies, is wasted effort. All information is costly; information is the dominant call on resources; ideas of optimality must therefore be extended to information and information channels, ie, organisations (Lamberton 1993b, 1994).

This chapter has focused on conceptual aspects of the role of information and organisation. I have done this in the belief that information economics has a further contribution to make to research and policy in urban development issues. Several interconnected topics could be given top priority:

1. Information asymmetries: across space and social groups; between firms; and in the external relationships of cities.

2. Patterns of use and demand for communications services.

3. Property rights in information.

4. Information justice.

Topics 1 — 3 feature inadequately in research and to mention information rich versus information poor to the great majority of people invites an end to the conversation. Perhaps the recent United States Information Infrastructure Task Force report, *The National Information Infrastructure: Agenda for Action* (1993) will stimulate wider debate. Although *The Economist* describes this report as "a slight but sober distillation of earlier enthusiasms" (1993: 92), like those earlier enthusiasms, it leaves many questions unanswered.

In the spirit of cyberspace, we are told that all things are possible with the new infrastructure, in which the new machines are dominant and people are added almost as an afterthought. In the United States the very costly superhighways of pre-election days have now been discovered, miraculously, to have been created already by the private sector and to be in need of only a little "topping up" by government. Nothing is said about how to create the appropriate regulatory and incentive structures, nor about how to extend the universal service concept to ensure that information resources are available to all at affordable prices. In brief, this agenda is in the enabling tradition. It is overconfident about the implicit technological forecasts and says little about the costs involved. And it has the fundamental flaw of that genre: failure to fully appreciate that some will be enabled more than others in the growth and development race.

Such costs and asymmetries have an important bearing on the nature of cities in the future. However, we must recognise the very real difficulty in giving meaning to the optimal use of information. We sense potential for major contributions to resolution of conflict, cooperation, invention of sustainable, productive systems and progress with organisational design.

Realisation of that potential depends upon the technocrats and embezzlers of knowledge being kept in check. Whichever way this balance eventuates, the map of the city of the future will be basically an information and communication map.

Chapter 5

THE EMPORIUM'S NEW CLOTHES:
Retailing, technological change and urban development

Alastair Whyte Greig

The evolving nature and form of retailing within Australian cities continues to be strongly affected by demographic factors and patterns of urbanisation. However, recent micro-electronic related technological advances are also affecting the relationship between the retail sector and urban development. The decisions made by key actors within the sector affect a wider constituency of urban consumers and producers than previously. This chapter explores some recent developments within retailing and examines the role of micro-electronic related innovations in altering the relationships between retailing and its customer and supplier base. These relationships, combined with a growing internationalisation of the economy, will have important implications for activities traditionally located within Australian cities.

The chapter begins with a review of recent research literature on retailing and notes the neglect of the retail sector by many contemporary social theorists who have focused on the importance of consumption. The changing structure of the Australian retail sector is then outlined, which sets the context for a discussion of the relationship between retailing, technological change and urban development. The chapter concludes that the most important technological developments within retailing are often the less visible "backward" interlinkages between retailers and suppliers, rather than the more visible and more widely reported links between the retailer and the final consumer.

I   Existing Literature On Retailing

Recent literature on retailing has documented a wide range of developments which have affected the sector over the past two decades. These changes include ownership concentration, industry competition, the structure of contemporary retailing, the rise and fall of various forms of retailing, locational decisions, as well as the adoption of new micro-electronic related innovations designed to provide more sophisticated product and distribution information and speed up transactions both to and from retail establishments. However, much of this research tends to examine retailing in isolation from wider social and economic processes, or else it tends to assess the impact of a specific phenomenon in an atomistic manner, divorced from other retailing developments. This chapter brings some of these developments together in a more holistic manner in an attempt to assess the impact of these various milieux on Australian urban structures.

The past decade has also witnessed the recognition within cultural studies of the importance of shopping and consumption patterns in (post)modern urban society. This field has been at the forefront of attempts to place retailing, shopping and consumption at the centre of an analysis of the conditions of everyday life. Many postmodernists have argued that consumption patterns, rather than production patterns, are the crucial determinants of identity formation, while others have pointed to the relationship between consumption and the "plasticity" of identity. Within these frameworks, consumption is more than the reproduction of labour; it lies at the heart of the postmodern condition. As a consequence, retailing and shopping malls have assumed greater importance as "cathedrals of consumption". It has been argued that they have usurped public and symbolic spaces previously devoted to civic and religious functions. No contemporary urban development project can attract either finance or a "flock" without appealing to the citizen-as-consumer.

In other accounts, shopping is regarded as one arena where the weak in a patriarchal urbanised capitalist society can exert some degree of power (albeit non-transformative power) and control, and an arena where the weak can employ tricks and ruses to "exploit their understanding of the rules of the system, and to turn it to their advantage" (Fiske 1989; Morris 1988; Shields 1992). This appeal to the consumer evident in contemporary urban environments is often seen as more democratic than previous religious or aristocratic appeals and motives (Jencks 1978). In addition, for some postmodernists, the apparent chaos of commercial shopping and consumerism in general represents a refreshing liberation from the drabness of much of what passed as modernism. These approaches, focusing on the meanings people attach to retailing and shopping, provide useful insights into consumption patterns previously ignored by mass cultural theorists. However, they tend to underemphasise the structure of the retailing sector and the variety of "tricks", "ruses" and strategies which different retailers employ in their search for profits in a highly structured, competitive, marketplace. They also tend to underemphasise the growing trend to privatise public spaces — such as shopping centres — and the forms of surveillance and exclusion used to screen the "genuine affluent consumer" from others such as the young and the marginalised. The dynamics of this interplay are often lost in many analyses of popular culture, leading to an overemphasis on "consumer sovereignty" rather than issues of citizenship rights.

In contrast, neoclassical economists as well as radical political economists have tended to ignore retailing as less significant than production relations. In these perspectives, a strict productive/non-productive dichotomy between spheres of economic activity consigns retailers to the derivative distributional role of mere passive recipients of goods produced further upstream by manufacturers. Senker (1988), in her analysis of the effect of retailing upon British manufacturers, has called for a reconsideration of this dichotomy, and has called for revisions in traditional economic theories in order that the active role performed by retailers in product and process innovation be taken into consideration. Recently, Mills (1992:1) has also sought greater recognition among industrial economists of the role performed by retailing, noting that it is an area of "relative neglect". He pointed out that in sectors involving final consumers "retailing practices may also be important – in enhancing or creating market power, or in exploiting market power that stems from other factors". Both Senker and Mills emphasise the importance of upstream relationships between retailers and producers in determining the range and quality of products available on the market.

This recognition of the role which retailers perform in influencing product and process innovation is only one key area which must be understood in order to appreciate the relationship between retailing, technological innovations and the evolving structure of the city. The concept of a production filière (Marceau 1990a) — which stresses the strategic linkages which companies engage in along a given chain of production from raw materials to final consumption — helps locate retailing at a crucial junction between the consumer and manufacturing producers. This approach also suggests that the relationships developed between retailers and manufacturers are important in the locational decision-making process within firms and, as a consequence, important for regional policy and employment policy. It also highlights the importance of retailing in the process of locational clustering within sectors around urban and exurban nodes, as well as the growing importance of competition between cities and regions (see Falk Chapter 8).

Consumption patterns have also been emphasised by a range of post-fordist theorists associated with the concepts of "flexible specialisation", "techno-economic paradigms" and "regulation". Most post-fordists are concerned with explaining how modern economies have successfully achieved periods of stability when the underlying structural dynamics of capitalism appear to generate systemic crises. While the differences in the approaches should not be underemphasised (Neilsen 1991) they all recognise that a given techno-economic substructure requires modes of consumption and socio-institutional mechanisms which ensure that production and consumption patterns correspond with each other. The absence of such mechanisms tends to lead to social disequilibrium and economic crisis and it is no coincidence that these theories have gained currency during the crisis of fordism from the early 1970s onwards (Roobeek 1987; Boyer 1988).

However, despite this recognition of the important role which specific patterns of consumption have performed in stabilising particular models of capitalist development, the area of consumption (and the role of retailing) has remained a neglected field of study among post-fordist theorists. Within Australia, the "post-fordist" literature has been dominated by the debate between John Mathews and his critics over the significance of new technology and new production relations at the enterprise level. As a consequence, the concept of post-fordism as a broader social construct has received relatively less attention. A similar complaint has been made of the European literature on post-fordism and flexibility. Gibbs (1992: 6, 9) has argued that the treatment of retailing within this body of literature has been inadequate:

> Given that the era of mass production (or Fordism) was supposedly directly linked with mass consumption, it could be expected that more would have been said about the forms of consumption under post-Fordism ... In total, there has been little theorisation of the effects of consumption changes on the durability of the total regime of accumulation, even though a central theme of the regulation approach is that consumption and production systems must be in medium-term balance for a stable regime to be maintained.

He therefore calls for a broadening of the flexibility debate to include a filière approach, ensuring that consumption receives attention in discussions of social, technological and locational change. In this way, sectoral studies of post-fordism can help illuminate the more general discussion of post-fordism as a regime of accumulation:

> In the consumer goods sectors we need to look much more closely not only at what producers are doing, but also at retail policy within that sector, consumer choice, advertising strategy and marketing policy. In addition, there are important areas of work in relation to the role of technology in linking consumption patterns with retailer strategy and the subsequent impacts on producers. (Gibbs 1992: 24)

This review suggests that there is a need to supplement the growing literature on flexible production and post-fordism at the workplace with an examination of the constituting features of flexible consumption and flexible or post-fordist retailing. The filière approach can help bridge the gap between the abstract societal models of post-fordism and empirical data through assessing the relationship between flexible production and flexible consumption at the sectoral level. The remainder of this chapter will draw the outlines of such an approach within the context of Australian retailing, and will relate recent developments within the sector to technological change and locational patterns within urban Australia.

II   Urban Change and the Structure of Australian Retailing

This section explores aspects of urban development associated with the changing form, structure and influence of retailing. Store location is possibly the most crucial decision retailers and retail property developers need to consider in "setting up shop". It remains one of the key differentiating factors in an industry characterised by monopolistic competition (Davidson & Stewartson 1974). Retail property developers engage in extensive demographic research before choosing a location and this has spawned an entire research and marketing niche (Cardew & Simons 1982; Golledge 1984).

In line with Australia's demographic history and patterns of urbanisation, retail location has undergone a number of important transitions over the past century. The rapid suburbanisation of Australian cities in the 1920s and 1930s and the continuing reliance on mass public transport encouraged strip or ribbon suburban retail development in close proximity to major public transport nodes. The post-war long boom, increased discretionary spending power, urban decentralisation, suburban growth, the expansion of private transport, innovative architectural and building techniques, competition and diversification within the retail sector and, later, the search for outlets from large institutional investors, all laid the foundation for the process of regional shopping centre development, characterised by Sydney's Top Ryde Centre and Warringah Mall and Melbourne's Chadstone complex (Poulsen 1982). These regional shopping centres were usually free standing, offered a wide range of mass consumer products and relied on a key tenant, or anchor tenant — such as a department store and supermarket — to act as a magnet pulling in the outlying population. While regional and multipurpose regional megacentres — combining retailing with cinema complexes, international food courts, office complexes and leisure facilities — continued to flourish between the mid-1970s and the mid-1980s, more and more developer interest has been channelled into "revitalising the central business district and redevelopment of existing inner-city and suburban shopping centres — either through extensive malling or by consolidation and building" (Golledge 1984: 17). This interest helped fuel the overinvestment in CBD construction during the 1980s.

Thus, changing patterns of store location traditionally have reflected Australian urban, economic and demographic patterns. However, more recently a more pro-active role has been evident, with the perception that the retail sector has the ability to attract consumers and sell other commercial space. In Britain, Gardner and Sheppard (1989) have labelled this strategy for urban and regional development/renewal "retailing with everything". These public spaces are designed to attract the individual-as-consumer, and tend to emphasise the rights of private property over citizenship rights. Contemporary shopping malls and pedestrianised city centres increasingly are employing more sophisticated surveillance technology to interpret the legitimate use of such retailing spaces. An Orwellian atmosphere is evoked by Perth City Council's advertising campaign to draw citizen's back to the CBD: "See you in the city!" (Allen 1994). As White (1995: 37) observes, these commercial and technological innovations reflect other social changes within Australian cities: "Conflicts over amusement parlours and shopping centre activities are not isolated from wider structural developments. They pertain both to the increasing polarisation of wealth and poverty in society and to the overall distribution of community resources, including public space".

Social control and policing can occur more effectively in "enclosed" spaces relative to the openness of the streets. However, the demise of the traditional shopping strip has been predicted since the 1960s. Fisher (1984: 62-3, 1988) has recently added a new dimension to the demographically based prediction, arguing that technological, regulatory and institutional developments are encouraging further rationalisation within the Australian retail sector, which will "undoubtedly accelerate the demise of the traditional shopping strip" and result in the inevitable "accelerated consolidation of shopping facilities, into larger and fewer outlets operating from regional complexes."

However, both demographic and consumer trends suggest that this demise is less inevitable than Fisher suggests. Shopping strips — which suffer from less coordinated management relative to shopping centre developments — have begun joint ventures between retailers and small businesses in an effort to coordinate their marketing and promotional activities and improve their streetscape. For example, in association with the NSW Department of Planning, the Main Street program has begun a series of initiatives to: coordinate marketing; coordinate special opening hours; emphasise unique aspects of the area; provide a heightened sense of local history; approve cosmetic alterations; pay attention to business mix and lobby landlords; and strengthen the local chamber of commerce. Streets involved in the project include Oxford Street, King Street and Glebe Point Road in Sydney, and Lithgow, Jindabyne and Grafton main thoroughfares. Similar initiatives are being developed in Victoria (see *Inside Retailing* 11 March, 18 March, 15 April 1991; Hofmeister 1988). In addition, main streets are trying to discourage the establishment of large chain-stores on their beat, enhancing a marketplace feel and promoting a perception of diversity and exclusivity.

In effect, this is the response of strip shopping to the earlier discussed sense of contemporary shopping as spectacle and entertainment, and a response to shopping centre trends towards theme parks and simulated — or "controlled" — worlds. If the modernist Robin Boyd once viewed the commercial strip as a symbol of the Australian ugliness (Boyd 1960), then for the more post-modern Robert Venturi (quoted in Jencks 1978: 35), "main street is almost all right." It also represents an acknowledgment that there is more to (post)modern shopping than price busting and category killing. The accepted retail hierarchy of CBD, strip shopping, region centres and sub-regional centres is becoming more blurred as competition reduces certain advantages while opening up others.

These geographic trends reflect the variety of survival strategies adopted by smaller agents in response to a growing awareness of cultural fragmentation and the more polarised structure of the Australian retail sector. Furthermore, they need to be placed within the context of significant changes within the structure of the retail sector. Over the past few decades the general trend within most advanced capitalist countries has been for the service sector to increase its share of GDP relative to manufacturing. By the early 1990s, the retail sector employed 13 per cent of the Australian work force (1.1 million people), contributed 23 per cent of GDP and accounted for 39 per cent of private consumption expenditure; 52 per cent of the retail work force are women, and over half of this segment are part-time workers. Yet, in comparison, retailing in 1968-1969 accounted for about 14 per cent of the Australian labour force and the number of establishments officially declined between 1968-1969 and 1990-1991 from 137,000 to 122,000. However, beyond these aggregated statistics lies an extremely complex and fragmented process of change and this apparent decline belies the qualitative growth in importance of retailing. Official statistics also fail to record the "hidden" qualitative growth of "informal" retailing which has become more visible on the streets of Australian cities over the past decade as the social effects of economic restructuring manifest themselves. Figure 1 illustrates the point that generalisations concerning retailing as a whole must be qualified. As Marti and Zeilinger (1985: 356) point out, retailing is far from a homogenous activity: "the range of products is very wide, and the ways in which they are sold varies almost as much as the ways in which they are made". Different organisational structures also vary in a diverse range of ways. In addition, a filière approach suggests that retailing not only needs to be assessed in terms of its backward linkages with manufacturers; it is also important to examine the relationship between retailers and range of other agents involved in retailing services, such as building owners and managers, property developers and other agents involved in finance and town planning. Furthermore, corporate profiles often differ considerably between cities (although less so now than in the past). In other words, it is necessary to cast a wide corporate net in order to drag in the full range of players engaged in retail decision-making. The most visible and significant changes within the structure of retailing over the past quarter of a century have been associated with the growing power of the super-retailer. The locational and technological decisions of these firms have helped to shape the spatial patterning of retailing within Australian cities.

Over the past decade there has been a consolidation of large retailing establishments in Australia on a scale unparalleled in other market economies. In Britain, the top five retailers account for approximately 20 per cent of the market and the top 10 account for 26 per cent, while the top five Japanese firms control only 6.3 per cent of the market (Larke 1991).

"THINK OF IT — $2·5 BILLION WORTH OF DISAPPOINTED WOOLIES INVESTORS DESPERATE TO BUY INTO RETAILING..!"

The largest two Australian corporations control around 25 per cent of the local market. In the year ending June 1990, Coles Myer accounted for 15.6 per cent of the Australian retail market, while Woolworths controlled 8.4 per cent. Five other retailers (Franklins, Mitre 10, David Jones, BBC Hardware and Vox Ltd) held at least one per cent of the Australian market share. Woolworths, Coles and Franklins account for over two-thirds of non-perishable grocery sales. Expressed in terms of sales, Coles Myer are the twelfth largest retail chain in the world. This status is more remarkable considering that Coles Myer's geographical boundaries do not extend beyond Australasia. In terms of sales per capita, Coles Myer ranks first in the world, while Woolworths ranks fifth. Coles Myer employs over 140,000 people while Woolworths employs 71,000, making both significant players in the labour market (Australian Ratings Industry Profile (ARIP) 1991).

Despite this relative concentration and monopolisation, most commentators claim that the retailing industry remains highly competitive, especially in the area of food (ARIP 1991; Fisher 1988: 49; Gardner & Sheppard 1989: 163-4). With respect to the choice of competing outlets, it also appears that most retail sectors are competitive (PSA 1987: 64-5). Small niche retailers can enter the market on relatively little capital, through leasing a small space and obtaining credit from manufacturing suppliers. Some analysts claim that the retail market is well past saturation point and that many small retailers scratch a meagre existence through self-exploitation. According to one consultant, "we are an over-shopped, copycat, price driven, under-serviced industry" and by the end of the decade we will witness "fewer players in retailing, with up to half of today's retailers not existing in their present form or out of business" (*Inside Retailing* 22 April 1991). The fickle nature of small-scale retailing is illustrated in the large number of "for lease" signs displayed on main street windows during economic downturns. However, as with many other forms of small business, small-scale retailing is often a way of life for many people, and operates according to a different set of dynamics to large-scale capitalist corporations.

Among the most important developments to affect the structure of the retailing industry over the past few decades have been: the growth of self-service (or no-service) supermarket chains during the 1950s and 1960s competing with independent greengrocers, butchers, bakers etc (Walmsley & Weinand 1991); the growth of discount stores competing with traditional department stores and using direct trading instead of wholesalers (Cardew & Simons 1982, 152); and the dominance of regional and super-regional shopping malls with key anchor tenants over traditional suburban ribbon or strip shopping and the central business district, resulting in the decentralisation of retailing. Furthermore, intense competition among large multiples for a relatively static dollar has led to a decline in the middle ground of retailing, leaving space primarily for the small specialist or niche retailer. As a consequence, the retail market has become relatively more polarised, with concentration at the upper end and fragmentation at the lower end. Fragmentation at the lower end of the market has been accentuated by the growth of the phenomenon of "off-the-book" retailing, visible in the streets of most capital cities. These developments are far more significant than the 11 per cent decline in outlet numbers over the past 20 years would suggest.

As a result of these advantages and disadvantages, the retailing sector remains characterised by diversity despite the emergence and growing dominance of large-scale retailing. One consultant has even argued that mass markets have now disappeared. Echoing the claims of flexible specialisation theorists, Tony Joyce has claimed that mass markets "have gone, mass merchandising has gone and mass merchants will therefore eventually have to become category killers to survive" (*Inside Retailing* 22 April 1991). While this is possibly an overexaggeration, it reflects the growing trend towards flexible, diversified retailing, and suggests that the industry remains in a state of flux, with new opportunities presenting themselves across the retailing spectrum. As long as urban growth continues, whether intensively or extensively, retailing will continue to exploit new markets and demographic trends. Retailers have adopted much of the current terminology used in urban studies: Coles Myer have as part of their current corporate plan, "geographic 'infill' expansion" (see also Morris 1988).

The emergence of large retail developers as well as large retail merchandisers has also led to increased cooperation among groups of corporations against rival shopping centres (Cardew & Simons 1982: 156-9). As a result, spatial competition has emerged as a significant factor and the location of a major complex within the urban framework has become a more vital consideration as the choices of more mobile, car-oriented, consumers have expanded beyond the local suburban strip. The property development and building owners and management markets have expanded their power along with the growth of large shopping centres. Anchor tenanting, tenant mixing and mall entertainment are all crucial competitive factors in the ability of centre management to attract customers to one location rather than another. Over the past decade regional centres have rediscovered the importance of presenting shopping as a "spectacle" or as "entertainment" rather than as a hard-nosed, cold, competitive marketplace where "the price is right". This concept of spectacle has always been the key to successful department stores (Reekie 1993). In addition, new retailing facilities are often used as magnets for multi-purpose subregional complexes to draw in local employment to new office space. These spatial factors within the city also help explain why the retail polarisation which has resulted from the disappearance of the middle-ground has failed to unite smaller retailers against larger retailers. Many smaller players are drawn like a magnet towards the market which larger players attract.

These are only a few of the important changes which have affected the structure of the retail sector over the past two decades, and it is within this context that the application of new technologies and changing locational patterns within cities should be assessed.

III   Retailing and Technological Change

The relationship between micro-electronic related innovations and retailing remains an underexplored area within the humanities. Braham (1985: 123) accounts for this neglect through the fact that "the importance of retailing within the economic system has traditionally been downgraded, and its relationship to other parts of the system has been overlooked". In addition, retailing has often been seen as being traditionally a "very labour intensive industry" or a "low technology enterprise" (ARIP 1991: 21; Braham 1985: 123). Most observers have focused on the retail/consumer interface when assessing the impact of retail-related technological change (Reinecke 1982). Other commentators have focused on the long-awaited promise of teleshopping and home-shopping, while ignoring less "revolutionary" developments within conventional retailing practices. This section begins with an assessment of teleshopping and its potential effect upon urbanisation before examining the retailer/consumer interface. Finally the section will explore the retailer/manufacturer interface and its more long-term impact on Australian urbanisation.

1   Teleshopping and urbanisation

Since McLuhan and Toffler the world has been waiting for the introduction of the electronic cottage. This promise of the electronic cottage has also been adopted as a vision by the housebuilding industry, where tomorrow's smart houses simultaneously will be multipurpose centres of leisure, entertainment, consumption as well as workplaces (HIA 1990: 1). The telecottage would radically alter patterns of work and leisure as well as our use of urban space. An important component of this electronic cottage is teleshopping or home-shopping.

On the high side of optimism, teleshopping would transform the structure and location of retailing, diminish the importance of CBDs and regional shopping centres, encourage the growth of large warehouse firms, distribution firms, home delivery firms and other service organisations associated with teleshopping. Within cities, the only visible physical movement would be the function of distribution.

On the high side of pessimism, Carter (1987: 304) claims that this scenario is unlikely in the foreseeable future and that new technologies have had a far bigger impact on "the enhancement of conventional services". Others, such as Forester (1992: 31-2), have dismissed the potential of teleshopping on both technological and cultural grounds. Practical problems such as "complicated on-screen instructions, difficulties over payment systems, problems with arranging delivery times, and a lack of choice of products" have dampened the enthusiasm of both the providers and consumers of the technology (Gardner & Sheppard 1989). Arguably the greatest barrier to the diffusion of teleshopping is cultural: teleshopping advocates obviously dislike shopping! As Forester observes, teleshopping ignores the psychology and sociology of shopping as well as failing to appreciate that there are people who shop for pleasure, leisure and social interaction. Popular culture theorists such as Fiske (1989) argue that shopping is more than a cash transaction: it is a form of popular guerrilla warfare, where issues of power, identity and spectacle are played out. The unemployed and marginalised use spaces in town centres and shopping malls just as much as those with the power to buy (even though they use and read these spaces differently, and are read differently by the agents of management). Urban spaces are never simply used for the sole rational purpose assigned to them by town planners (Raban 1975).

The potential for teleshopping can be judged from the success of direct marketing. Although the Australian direct marketing industry is estimated to be in excess of $1.5 billion — and is far from mature — its potential growth appears limited to sections of the population either without time, ability or desire to shop. Other potential markets are isolated rural areas and the less mobile. Furthermore, certain product categories are more suited to teleshopping and direct marketing than others (Marti & Zeilinger 1985: 358). This assessment suggests that the impact of technological change will remain more significant in more traditional forms of retailing, as these forms will remain dominant for the foreseeable future.

2   Technological change and the retail/consumer interface

The application of micro-electronic related innovations and automation began to impact upon the retail sector during the late-1960s. Large complex organisations began using mainframes to handle the increasingly complex backroom operations of stock control and stock distribution between outlets (Marti & Zeilinger 1985). By the late 1970s micro-electronic related innovations began to alter the retailer-customer interface through the introduction of electronic point of sale (EPOS) technology (Larke 1991). Within Australia, the introduction of laser scanners and EPOS accelerated during the mid-to-late 1980s and by the early 1990s Australia ranked second in the world in the per cent of groceries scanned (ARIP 1991). EPOS spread quickly throughout all areas of retailing, from supermarkets, department stores, discounters, hardware stores, book stores, convenience stores and chemists. By 1993 electronic funds transfer at point of sale (EFTPOS) use had climbed to over 150 million transactions annually, and the number of terminals had leapt from 15,500 in 1990 to almost 40,000 (Cornell 1993).

For retailers, the advantages of EPOS include enhanced stock control, significant labour savings, more accurate labour scheduling and minimisation of operating overheads. Food retailing, in particular, is characterised by low margins and survival depends on quick response, rapid inventory turnover and strict cost control. EPOS has therefore become an essential component of management at the high-volume end of the market.

It has also been claimed that EPOS has brought improvements in customer service through quicker check-outs and more accurate, informative dockets. The expansion of EFTPOS also increases customer services through a wider choice of payment systems. For the retailer, EFTPOS settles transactions immediately and reduces administration costs (Gardner & Sheppard 1989). However, some consumer groups have been slightly more circumspect in their judgement of the technologies (pointing to the demise of individual and/or recognisable price tagging, disparities between checkout and shelf prices, operation of fewer check-out lanes, the potential for invasion of privacy etc). Although scanning firms (such as NCR, which controlled 45 per cent of the scanning market in 1991), banks and large retailers have been at the forefront of promoting EPOS and EFTPOS (Gardner & Sheppard 1989), they appear to have been accepted by retailers and consumers alike. The ATM, hailed as a financial innovation barely a decade ago, is now considered a "mature" product and is being replaced gradually by retailers' EPOS terminals (Cornell 1993).

EPOS scanning relies on barcoding as well as product and batch numbering. The barcode standard introduced in 1991 (Application Identifier Standard) carries 37 types of data such as batch numbers, serial numbers, in-house applications, purchase order numbers, shipping container codes, product dimensions, and delivery location. While the processing of such information holds productivity and efficiency promises for large retailers, they are hardly geared for smaller retailers with less complex inventories (Fisher 1988). Gardner and Sheppard (1989: 227-80) have also questioned the ability of large retailers to process and harness the plethora of information: "This 'information revolution could all too easily degenerate from being a 'technical fix' to a technical fixation, from collecting data for useful purposes to data gathering as an end in itself." One industry analyst claimed that administrative offices of some large British retailers are littered with piles of unanalysed data.

Marti and Zeilinger (1985: 352) have argued that it is this "behind the scenes" application of micro-electronic innovations which will have the greatest impact on the retailing filière. These changes could be passed on to consumers in the form of lower prices due to efficiencies resulting from better stock control. However, this advantage, needs to be weighed against the more visible likelihood "for a smaller range of goods to be stocked and eventually even perhaps some reduction in competition if the stronger groups use these advantages to achieve dominant positions in their own particular areas". While Carter (1987: 304) has also predicted an oligopolistic trend as a result of the application of new technology, arguing that EPOS and EFTPOS will result in ever larger and more efficient stores, he claims that this will benefit the consumer "by providing a very wide range of goods under a single roof, with consequent savings in time". Either scenario is possible and they should not be viewed as mutually exclusive. Much will depend upon the corporate strategy adopted by different retailers within their particular market sector (ie department stores versus discounters or category killers versus variety stores).

3 Technological change and the retail/manufacturer interface

Large retailers have been placing more and more pressure on suppliers to include barcoding on their products. For example, Coles-Myer approached their suppliers in 1991 with the message "No barcode, no business". It can be argued that the most important socio-economic impacts of new technology have been these less visible "backward" linkages between retailers and suppliers. As noted in the introduction of this chapter, this aspect of retailing and its wider implications has received inadequate attention in the literature. This neglect is surprising given the role which retailing performed in providing a mass market for mass production during the first decades of the 20th century. Beniger (1986) has demonstrated how, from the turn of the century onwards, the bureaucratic control of mass consumption (large retailers "processing people past products", scientific advertising, use of data processing etc) were crucial for the stimulation and control of mass demand, as technological and organisational innovations began to dramatically improve productivity and efficiency within the manufacturing sphere. In addition, it is often forgotten that the stock replenishment methods used by post-war United States' supermarkets provided the inspiration for the Toyota production system (Sayer 1986).

The effect of retail-related micro-electronic innovations on suppliers goes far beyond the demand that manufacturing suppliers barcode products. These technologies are fundamental to retailers' efforts to introduce Just-In-Time (JIT) processes which enhance planning and scheduling systems, reduce inventories, demand smaller batches of more variety of products and improve quality control procedures. The consequence has been that large retailers are assuming greater control over aspects of upstream processes that were once considered the manufacturer's sphere of responsibility. The hard and soft technologies which make this development possible are Quick-Response (QR), paperless trading such as electronic data interchange (EDI) and quality control procedures.

The competitive nature of the discount market, combined with retailers' frustration at the failure by manufacturers to achieve replicability of mass produced commodities, has forced Australian retailers to assume greater responsibility for quality control over their suppliers' products. From modest origins in the late-1960s, companies such as Woolworths, K-Mart, Target and Best & Less, developed sophisticated quality control laboratories which have become central to their purchasing strategy. All products must undergo strict quality testing before orders are placed (Greig 1991). As a consequence of this, retailers, especially discounters, have performed a catalytic role in heightening the awareness of quality among local manufacturing suppliers. These laboratories often act as manufacturing consultants.

In addition, EDI and QR, which link the retailers' ordering system electronically to that of the supplier, help reduce retailers' inventory costs. Linked with EPOS, EDI creates a total distribution control system, providing almost instantaneous information on product sales and stock replenishment needs. Among the benefits of EDI are the ability to carry leaner stock, the reduction of stock-outs, more rapid response to stock requirements and the consequent avoidance of lost sales by suppliers. As retail orders become more frequent, quicker and yet smaller, manufacturers are faced with the added burden of acting as the retailers' warehouse. Given the oligopolistic nature of Australian retailing (where the loss of one customer can mean commercial death) manufacturers have had little option other than adopt QR technologies. Coles Myer has also adopted QR in its food operations and it has been predicted that companies "who do not adapt to quick-response ... will almost certainly fall by the wayside" (*Business Review Weekly*, 8 June 1990; see also Marti & Zeilinger 1985: 358). Already, stories are filtering through to the retail press reporting how EDI has "revealed some shocking instances of supply breakdown by a number of famous brand suppliers".

The centralisation of large retail purchasing and distribution centres has also impacted upon manufacturing suppliers' locational decisions. For example, the closure of Grace Brothers' Sydney buying office in 1991 and its replacement by central buying from Myer's in Melbourne adversely affected Sydney manufacturers. As a consequence, locational decisions regarding purchasing can have far-reaching effects on employment patterns, especially manufacturing employment, within and across cities. K-Mart's Hoppers Crossing distribution centre is regarded as the future face of retail distribution. It is a joint venture with Linfox, and possesses full computer scanning, automatic dispatch and retrieval systems as well as EDI facilities, resulting in reduced labour costs and tighter control over suppliers. In addition, by 1991, the Coles Myer group possessed Australia's fifth largest telecommunication network, with data-, video-, and voice-links connecting outlets, offices, distribution centres, manufacturing suppliers and financial organisations (*Inside Retailing*, 25 November 1991). National Australia Bank has captured the accounts of leading retailers such as Coles Myer and Woolworths, while ANZ Banking Group has tied service stations such as BP and Shell. However, some analysts claim that Coles Myer's integrated EFTPOS base eventually could be used to challenge the dominant position of banks in certain financial products (Cornell 1993).

In order to guarantee future contracts with the principal retailers, manufacturers have been forced to adopt JIT techniques (such as leaner inventories) as a matter of survival. The infrastructure for developing such ongoing retail/manufacturing linkages is costly, as is the time involved in developing corporate trust. Consequently, manufacturers able to break into retail networks will be greatly advantaged compared to firms locked out of these relationships. Manufacturers unable to meet the demanding schedules of retailers have been forced to consider other options, such as operating their own factory outlets, or joint ventures in retailing. One industry expert has predicted that the further rationalisation of the retail industry will encourage more "supplier-oriented small stores or boutiques" to emerge, "designed to promote showcases of the suppliers' merchandise and first-hand feedback on consumer trends and preferences" (*Inside Retailing* 29 April 1991). The overall result is that there is currently a great deal of cross-fertilisation of activities between retailing and manufacturing, breaking down traditional boundaries of functional demarcation. Future trends suggest that national super-retailers linked with national brands will co-exist principally with small local multi-purpose firms coordinating local networks of clients and suppliers. In a locational and employment sense, the former will tend to be more footloose than the latter. One important implication of these trends is that urban and regional planners will need to pay greater attention to local corporate networking.

These relationships between retailers and manufacturing suppliers have clear consequences for manufacturing policy and employment patterns within regional towns and cities. The heightened importance of quality control, JIT and QR demands much closer and stronger relations between retailers and manufacturers. While price remains an important concern for Australian manufacturers competing in a more open, less protected, environment, there are other factors which will influence retailers' competitive strategies as well as the location of manufacturing establishments. In this more diversified and competitive market, survival depends more than ever on convincing the consumer that the local product represents better value than the imported counterpart, in terms of quality, price and service. However the relationship between customer and manufacturer is mediated through the retailer, who acts as the interpreter of customer needs and desires.

The range of factors influencing retail sourcing extends beyond price competitiveness, and provides Australian manufacturers with a number of advantages, relative to overseas competitors. One important advantage is the local producers' more acute understanding of the local market. Increasingly, retailers are seeking out long-term relationships with suppliers that employ sophisticated marketing tactics and have developed a well targeted customer base. The growing acceptance of concept stores, where manufacturers lease space within department stores, further highlights the functional cross-fertilisation within filières. Australian manufacturers have a natural advantage over foreign-based companies, being more attuned to the peculiarities of the Australian market. Another advantage accruing to local manufacturers involves less complex difficulties associated with overcoming quality problems. Most retailers have experienced problems monitoring quality from offshore facilities. QR demands rapid problem solving, yet goods landed from overseas cannot be returned to their source without considerable cost. An associated advantage held by local producers involves their ability to supply more flexible quantities of stock and, on repeat orders, smaller batches of greater variety after initial retail EPOS data is analysed. As noted earlier, in an effort to reduce inventories, retailers are using manufacturers as defacto warehouses. Local producers have a natural advantage servicing this requirement. Local producers can deliver much smaller quantities at a fraction of the cost. Finally, local producers have an advantage over delivery reliability. Retailers have increasingly tightened their scheduling requirements over the past few years, placing enormous pressure on suppliers, with penalties attached to late delivery. Overseas manufacturers are much less flexible than local suppliers in this respect. The spread of EDI will further enhance rapid shipment potential. Furthermore, despite productivity improvements on the waterfront, many retailers remain distrustful of their efficiency. It is therefore to the advantage of local retailers to encourage a healthy local manufacturing base. As noted above, retailers are rationalising their supply lists, eliminating those unable to comply with QR, and are strengthening ties and seeking long-term relations with the most credible, viable and trustworthy. Therefore, while price remains an important consideration in determining a total product offer, local manufacturers have clear non-price advantages. The filière approach to sectoral industrial development suggests that the future of local manufacturing and manufacturing location needs to take into consideration not only comparative productivity and efficiency between local firms and overseas competitors, but also the relationship between local retailers and manufacturers. The strength of this relationship has important implications for industry policy, and as a consequence, the future structure and form of Australian cities.

IV   Conclusion

This chapter suggests that the forms of flexibility which have concerned "post-fordist" theorists over the past 20 years have not been confined solely to the sphere of production. Australian retailers have been reshaping their organisational and technological structures in an effort to improve their efficiency and cope with the demands of a changing market. The effect upon the structure of the retail sector has been towards concentration at the upper end, and fragmentation at the lower end. Not only are product markets becoming more diverse, but retail strategies have also become more diverse. The relationship between retailing and manufacturing has become increasingly complex, and this chapter has explored areas where retailing has promoted change within the manufacturing sphere.

Micro-electronic related innovations have affected all aspects of retailing, from internal organisational and managerial procedures, to relationships with the customer, relationships with the "non-consuming" citizen and relationships with the supplier. The application of micro-electronic related retail technology has further tightened the relationship between retailers and their suppliers, and the oligopolistic nature of the Australian retail industry has left most local manufacturers with little option but to fall in line with large retailers' demands. However, the less visible aspects of technological and organisational development could prove the most important in their impact upon locational patterns and employment patterns within cities. While the power relationships between retailers and manufacturers appear to have become more asymmetric over the past two decades, the relationships themselves are vital for the future ability of Australia to retain a healthy local manufacturing base: a weak link will result in a "tourist-led" form of retailing and urban restructuring with more limited local employment opportunities (except, ironically in retailing); a strong link will promote a more dynamic form of urban development with potential for employment diversification.

Doesn't link Retailer-Mar-t
to "urban" issues

Chapter 6

CONSTRUCTION TECHNOLOGY AND URBAN DEVELOPMENT

Marton Marosszeky

Increases in building size and flexibility in their form and function are the major influences that have shaped cities visually and spatially in this century. As society has become increasingly urbanised and cities larger, increases in land value have placed economic pressures on development, promoting higher density land use, especially in the inner city commercial areas. The other factor which is promoting a higher density of land usage in the suburbs of Australian cities is the need to provide and operate infrastructure and community services more efficiently.

Cities provide the urban historian with evidence of past social, economic and cultural structures and institutions; however, the most tangible record is of past architectural styles and construction techniques. Relative to other areas of technology, construction has altered less in appearance, with most change taking place in the past 50 years. For example, it is only since the middle of the 19th century that some of the structures of the Roman Empire have been surpassed and many older cities have masonry structures that have been occupied for hundreds of years. However, it is important to recognise that there have been many less visible changes. Even in the construction of a brick wall, a myriad of innovations have improved efficiency in terms of waterproofing, thermal and construction efficiency. These improvements have allowed this type of construction to remain competitive with more recent materials and systems.

Apart from a few notable exceptions, construction technology has played a relatively passive role in influencing cities. Other factors have determined the shape of both the urban fabric and at a more detailed level, the structures within it. In other chapters in this book, Dingle and Frost discuss the effect on urban infrastructure of technical change, Greig the changes in retailing and their effect on development and Marceau the forces that have shaped the concentrations of business activities within cities in Australia. Technical developments in construction have enabled the urban fabric to accommodate these developments, while economic policies and pressures, regulations, zoning and social behaviour have tended to determine the form of cities.

In the two key areas of residential and commercial construction, buildings have increased in size and are more flexible in form and function. Increasingly intense land use has been made feasible by significant increases in the capacity of urban infrastructure in electricity, water, sewerage, transport and telecommunications. Improvements in construction technology have allowed more energy efficient buildings to be built from less material at lower unit costs. The increased efficiency in building construction together with rising affluence means that more space is built per capita now than in the past, thereby adding to the urban growth pressures which result from increasing population.

I   The Inner City

As cities grew in size, commercial activity drove up demand for inner city land, forcing values up. High land values led to intense utilisation in order to limit unit costs and this had the effect of pushing up both population density and building height.

Rome in the first and second centuries AD, estimated at one million inhabitants, (*Encyclopedia Britannica*, vol 10: 162) described by historians as a very crowded city, was the first to experience these pressures. The limiting factor for the height of inner city buildings was how far people were prepared to climb up stairs. After the great fire of AD 64, Emperor Nero decreed that buildings should be limited in height to 21.5 metres, sufficient for six floors. This suggests that before the fire, heights above this were not uncommon. These buildings were built of fired clay bricks laid in mortar, a technique developed by the Harrapan civilisation on the Indus some 1500 years earlier.

Prior to the development of electric lighting in the 19th century and air conditioning in the 20th century, all buildings had to be relatively narrow in their floor geometry, often incorporating light wells to ensure adequate ventilation, and natural light to provide the occupants sufficient visibility for their work. This applied to both residential and commercial buildings. Thus, six-storey, narrow planned, masonry construction typified inner city buildings in all the major cities of Europe and North America before the mid-19th century.

The development of the safety elevator in 1854 provided the opportunity for city centres to expand upwards. While elevators without safety devices had been used for centuries for transporting goods and miners, who presumably accepted this as an occupational risk, it was only when Elijah Otis invented the safety catch that elevators became acceptable for transporting passengers:

> He first demonstrated this invention publicly at the Crystal Palace Exhibition in New York in 1854. He had himself hoisted to the ceiling and then ordered the rope to be cut; the safety catch thus released engaged the ratchets in the guidance rails. (Cowan 1977: 249)

More than any other development related to construction, this invention created the potential for high-rise buildings. In the following 50 years refinements in materials technology in both concrete and steel and in structural design and foundation engineering, provided engineers with the opportunity for developing efficient tall buildings. Similar technical development was evident on both sides of the Atlantic.

Although Elijah Otis's safety catch was the key to the introduction of passenger lifts and hence created the opportunity for high-rise buildings, the space required for vertical transportation is one of the greatest impediments to buildings becoming taller. Schroeder (1988) undertook a theoretical analysis of lifts for tall buildings using various lift configurations. He found that, using quadruple deck lifts, elevator space requirements on the lower levels of a 104 level building take up 22 per cent of floor space while this increases to 58 per cent for a 214 level building. In the future, building height is more likely to be limited by economic considerations than by technical factors.

The first multistorey building in which the floors were supported by iron columns was William Stutt's Calico Mill in Derby, built in 1792-93 (Condit 1988). In structures of this kind the main motivation for using iron was to achieve a fireproof construction. Cast iron beams were introduced four years later. However in recognition of their limitations due to the brittle nature of cast iron, wrought iron with more reliable tensile properties was introduced in beams in 1810. Throughout the 19th century, wrought iron and cast iron had been used in many innovative structures. In 1856, Henry Bessemer's invention of steel with reliable ductility and higher strength at an economic cost led to Dorman Long and Co in England in 1885 producing rolled steel joists for construction for the first time. In spite of this, riveted compound sections made from wrought iron plate and angle were still available into this century.

In addition to improved knowledge about materials and structural design of the frame, an essential development was in the growth of knowledge about the interaction of structures and the soil supporting them. Leaning masonry towers are found throughout Europe, providing evidence of the non-uniform bearing capacity of the earth's surface. The development of the foundation raft and of modern piling techniques in the latter part of the 19th century provided the essential breakthrough, once again permitting buildings to go higher with confidence. The combined effect of these developments permitted the use of inner city land at higher densities than ever before.

Chicago — generally known as the home of high-rise construction — had experienced unprecedented growth between 1860 and 1890 with the population increasing from 100,000 to one million and further to two million by 1910 (Frost 1991: 104). In the midst of this period, the centre of the city was burned to the ground creating a rare opportunity for redevelopment. It was here, in the midst of this extraordinary urban growth that the development of the modern high-rise building leapt forward. The change from high-rise masonry construction to high-rise *skeleton* construction was well illustrated in the development of the Monadnock building.

In 1891 the Monadnock building was the tallest masonry building ever built. At 16 storeys, wall thicknesses at the ground floor measured 1.83 metres and due to the weight of the building and the inadequacy of foundations, the building sank approximately half a metre by 1940. The building still stands, a relic of a past era. The decision to build the building of stone at a time when steel construction was already becoming accepted was the client's. Shepherd Brooks, representing the client wrote to a business associate in 1892: "As to erecting a tall building entirely of steel, for a permanent investment, I should not think of such a thing" (Hoffman 1973: 160).

Today, *skeleton framed* tall buildings abound in most major cities and the structural systems used to build them vary in the extreme relying on prefabricated steel, pre-cast and cast-in-situ concrete or combinations of these two materials to achieve efficient solutions.

Manufacturing technology in steel has advanced to a level where custom designed sections, optimising the use of steel can be readily fabricated, producing more economic solutions than if standard sections had been used. In the case of the World Trade Centre, the 110-storey building built in 1973 used steel plate in the columns up to 150 mm thick. The steel columns were not prefabricated as individual elements but as column trees consisting of a three-storey-high section, 15 metres high and three columns wide. These were fully prefabricated with welded connections throughout. The prefabricates, weighing up to 56 tonnes, were then lifted into position and connected with high-strength bolts.

While steel was the main material in the very tall buildings of North American cities, concrete is the material that is most evident in the cities of Australia and Asia. This ubiquitous material with its almost infinite flexibility in form has been used to produce an extremely wide variety of structures. When combined with high-strength steel strand, the pre-tensioning of concrete structures enables designers and contractors to construct more efficient, lighter structures than those which can be achieved with normal reinforced concrete. Also, the ease with which concrete can be pumped over considerable distances has led to an increase in its use. The multiple arch structure of the Sydney Opera House, concrete domes of various configurations and elegant large span, arch bridges and tall buildings such as the MLC Centre in Sydney illustrate the flexibility of this material.

In the 1960s and early 1970s it was believed that concrete was a maintenance free material. However, recent experience has shown that in aggressive environments, the reinforcing steel is susceptible to corrosion causing damage that is unsightly and expensive to rectify. While off-form concrete was fashionable in that period, buildings using it have become soiled and many suffered extensive deterioration. It is now quite common to see concrete structures painted with protective membranes or stains to improve performance throughout the life of structures.

Prefabrication has become widespread in the construction industry as it provides an effective mechanism for accelerating construction and thus reducing overall construction costs. It is not only the visible structural or fabric elements that are commonly prefabricated. Every activity that can be undertaken off site is increasingly done so. Electrical wiring harnesses, prefabricated wet areas for both residential and commercial buildings, prefabricated furniture and fittings, pipework and conduits for air conditioning are among some of these. While prefabricates in concrete and steel are common, one of the main limitations relates to the sizes that can be readily transported by road in congested cities. An exception to this was the World Trade Centre built by the Port Authority of New York and New Jersey on the edge of the Hudson River. In this case prefabricated floor panels 18 metres by six metres were floated down the river and lifted straight from barges onto the building.

Both transportation and lifting equipment have developed rapidly to meet the demands of prefabrication on large projects. Lifting equipment both in the categories of mobile and fixed cranage have increased in sophistication, scope and capacity making it more economic to position components efficiently on site.

The material that has had a major effect on the appearance of buildings this century is glass. While glass was first widely used on a large scale in 1851 in the Crystal Palace in Hyde Park, London, the material has really only come into its own in this century. The glass used in the Crystal Palace was blown glass that was flattened out and was known as crown glass. Drawn and float glass processes were invented in the 20th century and the wide use of glass in buildings on what are called curtain walls has only been common since the 1950s.

Le Corbusier's (1964) vision of the role of glass in the modern city has largely been realised. Glass has come to play a central role in passive solar design, permitting sunlight to be converted to heat during the winter months, but the use of shading devices or coatings on the glass and the use of fans prevents it in summer. The use of glass has enabled designers to develop a much stronger visual connection between the inside of a building and the outside, creating lighter and better ventilated spaces than were possible in the past.

Technical improvements in material properties have continued to increase the flexibility and scope of glass usage. Heat strengthening and toughening enhance strength, enabling architects to design with larger panels. Laminated glass with films of various colours have further increased the architect's palette, and provided impact resistance and safety to the material. Further, to control heat loss and heat gain through glass, double and triple glazed units are now fabricated and glass is often coated with selective coatings to modify energy transmission properties. Most recently, the inclusion of liquid crystal technology offers the possibility of altering the properties of glass walls in terms of their energy transmission and their opaqueness. This affects both privacy and light. Current development aims to provide a material that is, with the aid of feedback, able to respond to external stimuli and moderate internal environments. These developments have all significantly increased the usage of glass in buildings.

The development in all the building services — the combination of elevators, artificial light and controlled air — have enabled architects to design buildings which fully utilise the potential provided by material and construction techniques in modern cities. The development of air conditioning has taken place this century with a very early precursor being the system of heating and humidifying of the air at the Royal Victoria Hospital in Belfast in 1903 (Cowan 1977).

Building size and configuration can be unlimited both in height and horizontal extent enabling a much higher density of use than in the past. For example, in some large cities it is possible to roam over large distances, starting from a transport terminus and then moving from building to building without stepping into the outside atmosphere:

Underlying technical advances in almost every field has been the development of computer technology. Before the computer age, engineers developed approximate analyses for complex structures or simplified the structural form so that its behaviour could be predicted by theory at the time. Even large structures were built using simple structural systems that could readily be analysed or approximated.

> In 1866 W H Barlow built a parabolic arch for London's St Pancras Station with a span of 74.4 metres, still the greatest in any European terminal. These structures could not, however be accurately designed by the mechanics then known, and in 1865 J W Schwedler used the principle of the three pin arch for the first time in two German railway stations which rendered the arches statically determinate. (Cowan 1977: 53)

In the case of tall building structures, approximate solutions were obtained on the basis of iterative analysis. In 1966, an approximate structural analysis of the Australia Square building, 46 storeys high, took an engineer one year to complete. By 1976 a much more precise analysis of the 60-storey MLC Centre was completed by a computer in 43 seconds after data had been prepared. While the first data set may have taken a few days to prepare, subsequent analyses of a slightly modified structure only required an hour of data modification permitting the optimisation of the design. This ability by engineers to model, analyse and design structures by computer has provided the basis for the rapid development of large and complex structures both in buildings and in civil works.

While the earliest applications of computers to the building and construction sector were in areas of engineering analysis, this was soon followed by engineering design. As this technology continues to rapidly develop, the capacity to undertake increasingly complex tasks is making further inroads into design, documentation and quantity measurement. One of the greatest challenges in the design process during documentation is to effectively coordinate the many individual specialist designs. Computer technology can assist by overlaying the individual designs and alerting designers to potential conflicts. Architects in general practice now find that documentation by hand and by computer are equally cost effective and expect that computer documentation will become more efficient in the foreseeable future. In specialist areas of practice this has been the case for some time and projects are routinely fully documented on computer. When this is overlaid with the rapid developments in measurement, allowing quantities to be automatically taken from drawings, computer technology is set to make very significant changes to the design and documentation process and to the roles of the design professionals. The next stage in development will be achieved when knowledge-based software is effectively integrated with analysis and design software, permitting design optimisation on the basis of the best experience available.

In special purpose buildings and structures both architectural form and structural solutions are more varied than in the past. In larger span structures concrete is often pre-stressed to reduce weight and section size, promoting efficiency in terms of material usage and in some structures such as stadia, bridges and towers, the achievement of more elegant solutions than could be achieved with simple reinforced concrete. Other unusual structural forms rely on cable stays to provide necessary strength. These combine with the tensile capability of steel or other synthetic cable materials with tent like structures, shells or decks in a wide array of striking structural solutions. Whereas in the past, the size of buildings was limited by technology, this is now rarely the case. Planning and cost issues tend to be the limiting factors.

II   Housing

One of the areas where construction techniques had a more deterministic effect on urban form is in high-rise mass housing. This occurred in situations where housing demand was extremely high and urban space limited. In the first decades after the Second World War, in Europe and the Eastern Bloc the form of mass housing was dictated by production techniques and the drive for efficiency in construction more than by any other factor. These conditions have been repeated in the rapidly emerging cities of Southeast Asia.

In post-war Europe the housing solutions that were realised were also greatly influenced by the philosophical position taken by leading architects such as le Corbusier and Mies van der Rohe. They were attracted by the then current ideas of modernism, industrialism and social idealism: "Repetition dominates everything. We are unable to produce industrially at normal prices without it; it is impossible to solve the housing problem without it. The builder's yard must become a workshop. . ." (le Corbusier 1971: 220); "It is not so much a question of rationalising existing working methods as of fundamentally remoulding the whole building trade" (van der Rohe 1924: 81).

High-rise housing was favoured by a wide variety of interests. Town planners who wanted to contain urban sprawl, architects bent on realising Corbusian dreams, governments wishing to preserve the green countryside and a construction sector which could see the potential efficiency of building large projects compared to the traditional small scale of construction, all joined in what was to be later recognised as one of the major follies of the century.

The post-war period firmly established close links between the manufacturing and construction sectors for the first time. Governments in Europe encouraged technical development with grants, officially recognised accreditation systems to evaluate and legitimise new developments and publicly funded projects which provided a test bed for new ideas. Further, government involvement in housing on an unprecedented scale created new client organisations with large order books and these organisations naturally tended towards larger projects and larger suppliers. In this environment, capital intensive construction systems flourished, relying both on high levels of prefabrication and the intensive use of large-scale equipment in formwork and materials handling.

By the early 1970s however high-rise housing was thoroughly discredited in Europe and the United States with one of the most celebrated failures, the architectural award winning Pruitt Igoe project in St Louis, being demolished after it had been thoroughly vandalised.

In Europe, under the intellectual leadership of Habraken in the Netherlands, opposition to *mass housing* was gaining momentum. In his seminal book, *Supports* (1965), Habraken argued that the construction process had completely disrupted the natural relationship between dwelling occupants and their personal space, giving them no power to influence their immediate environment. He proposed that a more natural relationship could be re-established by separating the support and the infill components in multiple occupancy buildings, allowing the occupants to select materials and design layouts for the infill walls, fittings and finishes within a flexible support structure. This movement has led to the most creative body of housing research work worldwide, initially through the *Stichting Architekten Research,* or SAR in Eindhoven and is today carried on by the Open Building movement in Delft.

Opposition to much of the medium and high-density housing was on aesthetic grounds. Architects and others criticised the repetition in building fenestration and form, blaming it on prefabrication, the use of building systems and rational design tools such as modular coordination. In fact, little difference can be observed between in-situ and prefabricated buildings of the period, their overall appearance having been dictated by a rationalism in both design and production. There was a noticeable simplification in both the form and fenestration of all buildings in keeping with the utilitarian architectural styles of the time and consistent with the goal of minimising construction costs. It is only since the early 1980s that there has been a move back to more ornament and greater attention to the creation of variety in architecture.

Today, with the exception of Asia, new high-rise housing is found only in the centre of the largest cities (Kately 1988) generally serving the needs of upper middle class occupants, the group most likely not to have children. This form of housing is more generally accepted in all of the rapidly developing cities of the Asian region with notable success in Singapore. Population densities are generally much higher than elsewhere and generally, residential and commercial use are more closely intertwined. The rate of urban growth in these areas is very high, putting pressure on governments to maintain high rates of production with limited resources. In some ways this is similar to the demand-led post-war construction industry in Europe in which high-density housing was the norm.

In contrast, the sprawling suburbs of the United States and Australian cities have created their own problems. As a reaction to the urban slums of the 19th century, the 20th was heralded by the garden suburb movement. In the United States and Australia this translated into a generously spaced, low-rise suburban ideal. The widespread use of timber framed building, known in the United States as balloon-framing and in Australia as stud wall construction, in efficient low rise housing from the mid 19th century onwards, increased affordability and reduced the skill needed for building. This allowed new construction to keep up with demand, leading to the development of a spread out, highly urbanised society.

Timber resources have been more efficiently used. The development of a range of sheet products consisting of glued timber fibres, particles or laminates utilise any waste material that is insufficient in size or quality for milling. The use of timber in sheet forms has led to greater efficiency on the construction site. These products are also often modified to render them resistant to fungal and insect attack and fire, extending their life efficiency. Modern timbers are delivered to site, kiln-dried, stress-graded, dressed and generally in prefabricated wall frame and roof truss sections. Offcuts have been finger jointed into continuous sections, reducing waste and lower grades of timber have often been cut into smaller sections and relaminated to improve strength grading. All of these developments have combined to maintain the improvement in efficiency of house construction.

While outwardly less ornate, contemporary houses appear to be very similar to those built in the past. Yet in every other aspect, the housing industry has been transformed in the past 50 years. The two primary trends that have influenced this are prefabrication and the simplification of connections. The *do it yourself* or *(DIY)* movement of the past two decades has been a motivation for simplifying every aspect of construction, particularly the way materials and components are finished and connected, the two primary areas of trade competence. Plumbing and electrical systems have changed completely: water, sewerage and drainage pipes are available in PVC with simple glued or snap connections and the recent introduction of *soft wiring*, that does not need the special expertise of an electrician for installation, promises to transform this area as well. Doors, windows and stairs as well as kitchen and bathroom cabinets — all site fabricated a generation ago — are now usually pre-manufactured. Light-weight masonry blocks with improved acoustic and thermal performance are becoming more common. Generally, production is moving to the factory with the site process becoming increasingly one of assembly. This has enabled the industry to reduce the on-site construction period and has reduced the skills required for building.

III Building Services and Urban Infrastructure

Most of the basic techniques used in construction today had been tried by the turn of the century though in relatively simple applications. The Crystal Palace in Hyde Park, London, built in 1851 was an extraordinary development. Glass, wrought iron, cast iron and timber were combined in a simple, modular, prefabricated building system on a scale which had never before been achieved. Exceptional structures in prefabricated steel such as the Eiffel Tower (1889) and the Forth Rail Bridge (1889) and Sir Thomas Telford's wrought iron suspension bridge over the Menai Strait are all precursors of the sophisticated, larger steel structures of this century. Similarly the first concrete-framed tall building was built in Cincinnati in 1902 and the Centenary Hall in Breslau, built in 1911, had the first concrete dome to exceed the span of the Pantheon built 1800 years earlier.

The most visible way in which construction technology in urban infrastructure has impacted on development is in the construction of structures to support transport systems. Overpasses, overhead expressways, deep cuts in rock, bridges, expressways, expressway interchanges and tunnels are being woven through our cities to accommodate the expansion of the road and fixed rail transport networks. Arterial roads are widened, often with extensive wall structures to control noise and to separate residential areas from traffic. Parking structures, both as separate buildings and in the basements of modern office buildings have made a significant impact on building form and on the mix of space usage in cities.

In many congested cities around the world, new underground rail transport systems are being constructed under the existing city fabric using new tunnelling techniques. High-speed rail links between cities vie with air transport on short to medium inter-urban trips, and to permit these vehicles to operate at speeds in excess of 400 kilometres per hour, new structures are built to more accurate tolerances than in the past. These rapid transit links are often used to provide the basis for transport between satellite dormitory towns and city centres.

Developments in construction technology have combined to make these structures both increasingly affordable and possible on a larger scale. Large tunnel boring machines are capable of progressing up to 400 meters per day whereas the preceding drill and blast techniques moved typically at less than 10 metres per day. Similar comparisons abound, next to modern earthmoving equipment, the largest dozers of 30 years ago look like toys and their productivity is similarly disproportionate. Sophisticated formwork systems make concrete construction more affordable and complex steel prefabricates are manufactured using computer controlled techniques. In routine civil construction, culvert head walls, standard bridge beams and even retaining wall elements are all prefabricated. Reinforced earth retaining wall structures using prefabricated concrete facing elements have made it possible to build in confined spaces more economically.

In every area of both building services and urban infrastructure, improved control systems increase the capacity of existing systems, permitting higher levels of usage, often with improved flexibility and efficiency. In some recently developed plumbing fittings, electronic controls are used to reduce water consumption, thereby extending the capacity provided by existing resources and infrastructure. Similarly, more efficient lights and electronic equipment together with the use of higher levels of insulation have tended to reduce or at least stabilise the demand for power in buildings. Lighting in the perimeter zone is often automatically switched on or off depending on the outside light levels. Elevators are upgraded with the addition of modern control systems to increase capacity at improved levels of service. Air conditioning systems operate at higher velocities increasing capacity and the addition of chilled water or condensed water loops off central plant provide the basis for greater flexibility.

The increasing use of automated control systems and materials which respond either to natural stimuli or to feedback has led to terms such as *intelligent buildings* and *smart materials* being coined. While some of the developments in this category, such as talking lifts that greet you in a foreign accent on entry, are not so smart and have generally been disconnected, the overall trend is towards improved control and operational efficiency.

As an overall result, transport infrastructure is making increasingly significant impacts on life in the city. These include the visual effect of overhead structures and the separation roads and rail lines create. Noise generated by both road and rail movement is increasingly an issue and the disruption of existing local transport and communication routes alters local social networks.

IV   Environmental issues

Environmental issues in the modern city include wind funnelling in high-rise canyons, reflected light off glass building facades, access to sun, energy conservation and internal environmental quality.

In the past two decades, energy conservation has become a serious issue in the design of buildings. Since the world energy crisis of 1973 pushed up oil prices and raised awareness of the limitations to global resources, operating costs have become a more significant part of the building owners' overall budgets. While air conditioning has facilitated the construction of commercial buildings with large floor areas which do not rely on natural ventilation, this service in buildings accounts for the greatest consumption of electricity.

Building facade performance is one of the critical technical challenges that confronts the building industry today. Facades are complex, composite systems comprising metal framing, glass, sealant and masonry. Their structural behaviour is complex but to date their interactions with environmental forces have been analysed only at the simplest of levels. The present level of knowledge in this area is comparable to that in structural engineering at the beginning of the 20th century.

The facades separating the internal and external environments, regulate energy flows into and out of buildings. As such, they are critical to efficient thermal performance. In some parts of the world energy budgets for buildings are set by government, and building owners are penalised if their buildings consume in excess of regulated levels. In Sweden, the amount of insulation in dwelling walls is now specified at 300 millimetres; while, in the *laissez faire* policy climate of Australia, free market forces are slow to even recognise the benefits of double glazing in the colder, mountainous regions such as the Great Dividing Range.

It is highly unlikely that there will be any long-term reduction in the cost of energy in the future (Coates 1982). Population pressures on the globe will ensure both that energy remains a valued resource, and that the polluting effects of energy generation will be more stringently controlled. The application of environmentally conscious design criteria will increasingly be demanded and this will have an impact on both the form of buildings and the materials used in them. The visible impact on the built environment will be through the increasing application of passive solar design principles to buildings wherever possible. This will see greater use of shading devices to limit solar gain in the summer and both buildings and glazing being oriented to maximise solar gain in the winter.

In the inner city, overshadowing, access to sun and local wind funnelling are important issues as buildings reach skywards. Limits to building height on the basis of overshading can significantly affect property values, yet, guaranteeing sunshine in parks and open spaces is critical. For example, the height and configuration of buildings on the western side of Hyde Park in Sydney have been limited to ensure that sunshine reaches the park. In housing, the loss of privacy which results from overlooking is a similarly complex area.

Rogue reflections from buildings are an issue where reflected sunlight blinds drivers or where car headlights are reflected causing disorientation. Where a building reflects energy on to an adjacent one it can increase its heat load and where a new building overshadows an existing one, it will alter the air conditioning load. Questions of rights and responsibilities arise and overall, the resolution of conflicts which result from the environmental impacts of one property on surrounding occupants is attracting increasing attention from the law.

The other aspect that is becoming of increasing concern is the quality of internal environments. The growing occurrence of *sick building syndrome* is evidence of the fact that there are aspects of environmental quality that need to be further explored. Fresh air quantities are a critical issue, especially in new buildings where gases emitted from construction materials and from new products can cause health problems. Also in industry sectors where occupant density is increasing, there is a need for increased fresh air intake. All indications are that this issue, while still in its infancy, will become a major concern in the next decade.

V   Conclusion

The past century has seen the fabric of the modern city change as perhaps never before. This has reflected the economic, social, technical and cultural changes of the period. Developments in construction technology have, by and large, done little more than assist in the implementation of these changes, yet the construction sector and its efficiency impacts on almost every part of the economy. The buildings themselves and the urban fabric define important aspects of our work and leisure. The cost of construction, operation and maintenance of buildings and infrastructure impact on the economic efficiency of every activity in the economy.

Our ability to build large, complex and flexible structures is a function of several independent developments. Advances in the sciences of materials have provided stronger and lighter materials with reliable properties. The development of accurate models for structural analysis and design underpin the capability of structural engineers to design the complex structures of today. New high-performance materials in the form of alloys, composites and ceramics continue to offer new possibilities for architects and engineers. Developments in building services provide suitable artificial environments and transport and communication infrastructure provide the basis for increasing efficiency in access. All of these are essential ingredients for the efficient functioning both of cities and of large buildings within them.

Advances in construction technology have been, in the main, stimulated by economic forces to either improve the efficiency of construction or the utility of built assets. The demand for greater capacity in urban infrastructure creates the challenge for improved control systems to improve efficiency of use and the challenge to construct new structures within cities with a minimum of disruption.

To minimise disruption and construction time, activity is generally being transferred from site to factory. The manufacturing environment offers the benefits of different technologies and an environment that is conducive to better quality control. New materials and products tend to be lighter, stronger and more durable than their predecessors.

Environmental issues are among the most important faced by the industry. The domination of the motor car over all other means of transport has created a challenge for designers, and policy-makers alike, to make the city of tomorrow more accessible to its pedestrians. Environmental design is a pressing challenge, the need being to design more energy efficient buildings which are based on passive solar design criteria.

Chapter 7

TECHNOLOGY, INNOVATION AND THE CITY:
Three analytical approaches

Jane Marceau

Cities and city regions have long been recognised as the motors of economic growth. The density of population, the development of specialist skills and the concentration of capital in cities seem to be the basis for innovation in many industrial and science fields both in the past and in the 20th century. Experience especially over the past half century, however, has shown many changes in the relative positions and strengths of cities as the industries they have specialised in have relocated both inside countries and across national borders or transformed their operations. "World cities" such as New York, London and Tokyo have emerged as leading providers of financial services (partly perhaps as a result of their huge deposits of capital) with second-tier cities such as Sydney growing in importance in regional markets. Within areas of Europe — the north of the United Kingdom and France in particular — and the northeast of the United States, recent decades saw the decline of the "rust belt" cities as their heavy industry relocated. To some extent these same cities especially in the United States have re-emerged as "knowledge" cities, generating employment through their leading position in the production of the technologies such as micro-electronics and biotechnology which are at the heart of the emerging techno-economic paradigm. In other cases there have been clear changes in the position of whole regions. The growth to prominence of "new technology areas" such as "Silicon Valley", which is not a city in the traditional sense, has pushed policy-makers into analysing more carefully, job generation and hence development processes. The instability of regions whose prosperity was entirely dependent on policies which subsidised industries developed under earlier industrial conditions (cars, tyres, steel) proved how difficult it was to retain industries initially attracted to an area by the availability of cheap labour, land or other resources, again prompting policy-makers to reconsider their approaches.

Similarly the instability of urban and regional development and the many and rapid changes in city and regions' relative positions (both nationally and internationally) have to be seen in the context of the waves of development of "world capitalism". Capitalist industrialism has been said to have been born in Europe and grown to new power in North America. The "third wave" of capitalism however, seems to be the "age of the Pacific" (David & Wheelwright 1988).

Over the past two decades much economic power has shifted to the Western side of the Pacific. The rise first of Japan and then of smaller countries in East Asia has radically affected the distribution of world economic power and to an increasing extent, the relative position of many cities. What happens in the Kansai region of Japan is now as potentially as important for neighbouring countries' cities, as any event that occurs in Europe. Before the Kobe earthquake of February 1995, the Osaka, Kobe, Kyoto region had a population similar to that of Australia but a GDP larger than that of Canada and nearly twice that of Australia.

These shifts in the capital concentrations held by cities have occurred in conjunction with major changes in the technological paradigms underlying much economic activity and with the beginning of processes of globalisation. Some economic organisations have "stretched" their production or service activities across several regions of the globe while at the same time the ways in which much industrial activity is managed by companies has fundamentally shifted. Often referred to as the creation of a "post-Fordist" organisational paradigm, dependent on flexible and altered inter-company arrangements, this shift has had and will continue to have important repercussions on the organisation of production in industrial countries everywhere. Hence it will greatly affect what happens in cities.

Australian cities will be much affected by the growth (spearheaded by Japan) of a development corridor which extends from northeast Asia down as far as Australia. The high price of the yen has increasingly dictated the "export" of production from Japan to other countries of the region (the increase in Toyota's production of cars in Australia announced in March 1995 is further evidence of this export trend). Much employment in cities in Australia then will be determined by companies headquartered elsewhere and which face an increasingly volatile and uncertain world.

At a more local level, it is evident that the sociology of organisational change is inextricably linked to the politics of industry development dominant in a company's environment. This does not mean the politics exclusively of "regional or urban" development policies (such as provision of labour or infrastructure subsidies, cheap land, tax holidays etc) but the national and international politics which determine a general public policy stance towards activities in a given territorial arena. As with all politics, the outcomes, the bargains made, reflect the relative power of the players in both the international sphere and in the national arena where development decisions are made, as well as reflecting the ideological predilections of policy-makers. Moreover, any particular "region" or arena is composed of the policies of numerous players in both public and private sectors and contemporary bargains made must take account of and reflect the outcomes of earlier skirmishes.

The different elements of the bargaining equation in a given region or locality have to be regarded both as coexisting and as interacting. The influences on location have become both more complex and more closely interrelated, whether one is considering " local" (understood in the broad sense) or transnational activities. While it is now well established that the "territory" of any particular area has to be considered as a function of public policies and politics as well as of the decisions of private economic actors (Scott & Storper 1986), it is now evident that, the international context of and influences on public decision makers has to be an equally important part of the analysis. International influences, for instance, impact on the interactions between national and regional State authorities whose decisions in turn are much affected by electoral consideration and the local structure of government business relations. The decisions of private sector actors also in turn take account not just of either international or national business "environments" but of the particular mix which emerges in given territories over specific periods.

At any point these outcomes can be rechallenged either by the entry of new players or because existing players put together new arrangements which in turn are challenged by external changes or the relative position of other players, again in both public and private sectors. The outcome in any spatial area may thus be seen as the result of the activities and interaction of four major groups — producers, users, knowledge producers (public sector) and regulators (van Tulder 1989), whose activities are more or less closely articulated in any geographical area. Rather than being seen as a movement from " location (or 'territory') A" to "location ('territory') B", the process must be conceived as a continual dynamic, as a series of temporary "outcomes" each of which has immediate effects on others' activity and therefore contains the seed of change.

I   Innovation and Its Analysis

In these conditions it is no surprise that concern with local development is on everybody's agenda. In the last few years of the 20th century local development seems to most analysts to be increasingly dependent on innovation. Much has been tried including the creation of science parks, subsidies for research and development (R&D) and provision of facilities, often with subsidised rents. Universities have been encouraged to improve their links with local industry, while moves to enterprise bargaining have been thought to encourage a more flexible and responsive labour force. Cities are undoubtedly high-technology locations and generate both innovation in technology and the industries which diffuse such innovations.

Despite their best efforts, however, the planners of city space often find that their best efforts at encouraging innovative activities do not succeed to the extent hoped. This chapter suggests that a principal reason for the failure is that inadequate analytical tools are used, that the complex nature of the phenomenon of innovation and the multiplicity of actors concerned means that not one but several analytical "lenses" need to be applied. The lenses suggested here view the productive world of the city in terms of its organisation into clusters, chains of production and complexes.

Each lens alone gives only a partial vision and leaves the urban planner overly dependent on historically or comparatively based analyses which have little predictive power in modern Australian circumstances. One lens means only partial vision because technology, far from determining spatial changes in economic activity, is merely one element in what is a very complex equation.

The complexities of the equation mean that it will always be extremely difficult to predict future location patterns of both industrial and producer service firms and hence what will happen to the productive base of cities. City planners using only one approach or "lens" in analysing the problem of development can no longer say they ever could be sure that their policies will attract either new or relocating companies to their jurisdictions. Contrasting forces are at work. Recent studies both in Australia and internationally have shown, for example, that even the introduction of Just-in-Time (JIT) management technologies, often expected to both encourage leading firms to move to greenfields sites and to force suppliers to move to their immediate environs, may have different outcomes as producers develop alternative strategies (Greig 1992; Mair, Florida & Kenney 1988; Marceau 1992a). On the one hand, evidence on the evolution of technologies in such major manufacturing and assembly industries as automotives suggests that there may be a relocation both of assembler firms and their principal suppliers as the assemblers seek to impose new disciplines in both quality and delivery and in responsibility for the design of products. On the other hand, it is also clear that forces released by the same new competitive pressures and technologies are reducing the number of suppliers such that there will soon be only a small group of major companies producing in Australia for the industry as a whole. This will mean that new organisational strategies have to be developed as the suppliers cannot be placed close to all their clients. The situation is one of constant bargaining between companies of different market power and the technologies adopted are likely to be at least as much a function of this bargaining as of any "technological imperative".

Further, while manufacturing acts as a magnet for the location decisions of many service activities, and notably for producer services, the organisational possibilities opened up by advances in information technology have made the relationships still more complex. In accountancy firms, for example, information technology was first used for internal organisation purposes but as the technologies matured and as client firms improved the compatibility of computer systems, external links grew in importance (Daniels 1991).

In Australia the choices made will be even more complex because of the distances between major production locations and the push to export to the Asia-Pacific region. New planning approaches which take account of the constant bargaining now taking place not only locally but internationally in our region and the impact of the broadened organisational possibilities resulting from technological change must be developed. Special incentives may be needed, for example, to encourage multinational firms to locate their regional headquarters in Australia even though the high-grade telecommunications infrastructure essential to their operation is already available.

New approaches to planning will thus be needed whether the issue is the provision of infrastructure such as roads and rail, of commercial space or of housing and other public facilities. This chapter, working from the perspective of firms (since these are the central decision-makers) indicates that effective approaches can only be properly developed if there is better understanding of the complexities of the relationships between the choice of technologies by firms and the major players with whom they interact. The analytical frameworks described below seem the most useful in assessing the costs and benefits of particular choices so that all players, both public and private can bargain more successfully.

This chapter, of course, cannot deal with all technologies and the discussion is therefore limited to changes in core manufacturing and distribution technologies and the organisational modifications that seem to be associated with such transformations since these have the potential to liberate companies from the locational constraints of the past while at the same time providing new productive challenges. Further, as Falk (Chapter 8) points out in his contribution to this volume, there are many differences both between cities and different city areas in Australia as elsewhere and the lenses used must be adjusted accordingly.

II   The Background Situation: Core Technologies and Changing Organisational Systems

In recent years, as the high degree to which an economic system is dependent for growth on changes in technology has become apparent, an important debate has developed about the implications of technological transformation for the spatial distribution of industrial and service activities. As voters have increasingly seen governments as responsible for the well-being of the economy, public authorities have become concerned with trying to ensure a reasonably equitable distribution of economic activity over all geographic regions. In Australia this concern was seen in the Whitlam Government's creation of a special Ministry for Urban and Regional Development and attempts to spread population and economic wealth-generating activities over areas that in many cases crossed State lines.

Until the mid-to-late 1970s most regional policies were based on the recognition that changes in the international economic system and the international division of labour meant that many major companies were "foot-loose" and unless subsidised, likely to move to low-wage areas of the world. Regional policy, which in Australia has been largely urban policy, was thus based on developing mechanisms to encourage business to relocate to new areas within the country or to remain in established districts, thus pitting each region against competing ones, both nationally and internationally. While Australia was long protected by tariff walls from the full effects of the international search for cheap labour (as seen in the United Kingdom for example), the dismantling of the protective system has again raised questions about location.

In the 1980s location decisions by large companies were affected by the emergence of two new factors. One, and the one which most concerns this chapter, was fundamental changes underway in the physical technologies underlying the established organisation of the productive system. In Dosi's (1984: 17-9) words, "the technological trajectory had shifted and changes were no longer of degree but of direction": industrial organisation shifted across to a new technological paradigm. Firms using the traditional form of enterprise which had been competing essentially on price and a long-established system of production (typified by Ford's vehicle assembly methods) had to shift to competition not on price but on quality, technological advancement and quick response to changed conditions. Organisational changes are being made accordingly.

Second, not only did the world economic system as a whole begin changing rapidly but the very underpinnings of many firms' organisational frameworks and production assumptions were challenged by altered competitive conditions. These were notably the emerging preference of wealthy consumers for niche market products rather than the mass market ones on which many powerful enterprises had built their fortunes and the corresponding advantage given to smaller and more innovative firms and firms organised on other models. At the same time special assistance was provided by public authorities for new and smaller companies.

Thirdly, observers began to recognise that the economic success of Japan was achieved with a very different "business system" (Whitley 1990, 1992) from that dominant in the West. In conjunction with the new technologies, adoption of central elements of the "Japanese system" meant a move by some major companies away from the large and hierarchical forms of productive organisation of dominant firms in the United States and much of the West. Downsizing and the associated increased outsourcing meant greatly changed relationships with suppliers and clients as well as altered modes of the internal organisation of labour. These changes became summarised in the notion of "post-Fordism" or "flexible production" as the emerging form of productive organisation. Flexible production systems are often associated with spatial alterations in the distribution of activity, as has frequently been noted in relation to Japan and in areas of overseas Japanese investment (Kenney & Florida 1988). Carried by a "domino" effect that system, at least in a modified form, has gradually been adopted by most major companies such as those of the auto industry worldwide (Marceau 1992b: 125-32).

Planners also learned lessons from other productive models. Research in countries where company form had not been part of the dominant paradigm, such as Italy and parts of Scandinavia, revealed the existence of thriving communities of enterprises organised on quite different principles to those familiar from the major corporations of the United States or United Kingdom. These alternative organisational principles were those of complementarity, interdependence and innovation, both in product and process, rather than cost-cutting and labour-shedding and hierarchical control, and the size of the firms remained small. These models sometimes seem transposable elsewhere. "Silicon Valley" is the best known example of a new industrial district outside the traditional areas and while the Valley was badly hit by the recession of the mid-1980s, a new wave of firm creations has since created more jobs than before (Saxenian 1991: 278-81), giving extra credence to the view that such innovative "milieux" can be both permanently innovative and recreated elsewhere.

1   The emergence of new core technologies

In general analysts of institutional and technological transformation recognise four new core technologies which have already become dominant or are poised to become central elements in the productive systems of firms and hence vital in the organisational and locational strategies chosen. Of the core technologies, micro-electronics, at the base of the technological superiority of many sectors, notably automobiles and electronics but also financial services, has had the most visible effects so far. Close behind, and a technology whose implications are now claiming the forefront of strategic attention, are the revolutions in telecommunications, notably through the convergence of computing and telephone. The last two core technologies, and ones whose transforming power is still less clear, are biotechnology and new materials, especially advanced ceramics, but also many others. Each core technology has a number of variants which reframe particular industries' productive capacities (van Tulder & Junne 1988).

The convergence of micro-electronics and telecommunications is important for the issue of the location of the emerging productive base because it transforms the range of organisational possibilities available to firms both locally and over long distances. The new range of potential organisational choices, in conjunction with changed competitive circumstances in Australia has encouraged many hierarchical organisations to reframe themselves to take advantage of the cost savings involved in JIT Management systems (see below), for example, and create new forms of productive activity geared to continuous innovation. The development of smaller enterprises has also been offered new possibilities by information technologies. Formalised networking, which may involve co- or close location by partners, is perhaps the best known of the new strategies on offer (Sole & Valls 1991).

Changes towards new forms of physical and managerial technology have been hastened in Australia by major government policy shifts over the past few years. Since 1983 dismantling of protection has, especially affected long-established major employers, notably the automotive and clothing sectors, and many city neighbourhoods have been badly affected as a result. Some urban areas, especially in Victoria, have suffered doubly as they were home to both of the sectors worst affected. The main features of the potential spatial effects of the shift to JIT management systems in the automobile, electronics and aerospace industries have been extensively discussed both in Australia and worldwide (Marceau & Jureidini 1992). While ultimate choices by the firms concerned have not yet been made it is increasingly evident that large assembly manufacturers, typified by the auto producers, may relocate to greenfields sites and attempt to insist that their major or first-tier suppliers join them, establishing plants within a maximum range of 200 kilometres or so. This choice can already be seen in the new geography of the French and United States auto industries and to some extent in Australia with the choice by Toyota of a greenfields site for its major new facilities in Victoria.

Many companies have also shifted to international markets. At the same time they have introduced new technologies and reorganised internally. The resultant downsizing spread even to the growing service sectors such as banking as they benchmarked to international standards. The results of such changes have been felt most keenly in the cities and have raised major policy issues about employment, transport and other policies linking work and community in urban areas in the new productive circumstances.

Decisions by firms to relocate from inner to outer city areas in particular often rely on increased public investment in roads, rail and perhaps airports for the transport of goods and better public transport systems to link new production areas with established housing zones. Indeed, even where companies decide to stay in established city areas new organisational methods have implications for transport systems. Since, for example, JIT supply can involve deliveries direct to production lines in a given order, sometimes at intervals of a few minutes or on an hourly basis, firms must be sure that traffic problems will not disrupt supply and factories must have several points of simultaneous access.

Even with adoption of new physical technologies and such managerial strategies as JIT, final decisions about where to locate are still much affected by the decisions of both public policy makers and major private producers who are competitors or suppliers. In turn, these depend partly on the other priorities of governments and the degree to which they wish to intervene — for instance by offering financial inducements for location, siting educational facilities in given zones, allowing tax concessions or subsidies for R&D or introducing stiffer environmental regulation — and on the degree of dependence of a supplier on its major clients and vice versa. The outcome depends on the bargains struck, both between clients and suppliers and between these and with the different layers of government which have a role in economic development in a federal country such as Australia, in conjunction with new technological possibilities.

The effect of major change in the physical productive technologies available to firms thus will not *of itself* have major effects on the economic life of a city. All depends on how the firms decide to put the new technological possibilities into practice, on the organisational form selected. Some of the possibilities depend on the supply of appropriate labour and variants of the Australian Council of Trade Union's (ACTU's) 1987 blueprint for change in established patterns of work, skill formation and remuneration, have been put into practice in enterprises which benchmark against international best practice. These companies include vehicle assemblers, some building contractors, steel producers such as Smorgons in Melbourne, paper manufacturers such as AMCOR and chemical producers such as ICI at Botany.

The results of the changes both in physical and management technology and labour market practices are still flowing through the system but their importance has partly been overtaken by the rapid changes which firms are making in their search for new markets in the Asia-Pacific region. The evolution of the productive structure in cities in Australia must be considered in relation to the broader picture of Australia taking her place in the Asia-Pacific region as a regional supplier of value-added goods and sophisticated services, as was suggested at the beginning of this chapter. Research by McKinsey & Company for the Australian Manufacturing Council (1993), for instance, has highlighted the emergence of new high-tech enterprises which have been "born global" and organise accordingly. In an earlier paper

(Marceau 1992b) I pointed to the creation of Australia as an economic "territory of tensions" and the outcome of these tensions is still in doubt. The future could see both the emergence of Marshallian industrial districts in the way suggested by Scott and Storper (1986) — and a few have already been discerned — and the creation of new regional growth poles in major industries, encouraged by effective public-private partnerships of the kind already visible in and around Gladstone in North Queensland (Riemens & Marceau 1992). And indeed it will probably see the decentralisation of production to greenfields sites in Victoria and elsewhere by traditional industries affected both by technology and "Plans" devised by the Federal Government for the vehicle and clothing sectors. Even the transformation by new production technologies and new markets of the wool industry, which is beginning to see the emergence of an associated high-tech textile industry, have major potential effects on the shape and distribution of urban populations outside the capital cities, in places such as Geelong.

Given the multiplicity of potential outcomes and the multifaceted interaction of the different factors at work, only one of which is technology, how are city governments to choose which areas to support and in which ways to offer that support? Much depends on the ways in which the changes in the economic fabric are analysed. This chapter outlines three approaches to the analysis of innovation which can be used to elucidate crucial areas of activity and hence to highlight the points of intervention if a promising industrial development or product or process innovation is to be helped to come to fruition and the local city economy is to benefit.

III   Three Analytical lenses

Several chapters in this book discuss innovations which have transformed Australian cities and greatly affected both their shape and functioning. They discuss, for instance, the different interrelationships between specific aspects of technology and urban design and functioning, such as changes in transport technologies and the impact of telecommunications on working life and journeys to work. This chapter presents rather three possible sets of analytical "lenses" which are useful to describe and evaluate the innovation processes operating in a given city or region and hence to inform policy-makers choices in the search for city economic development. These analytical lenses view the productive world of the city in terms of its organisation into *clusters*, *chains of production* and *complexes*.

The new literature on innovation has come increasingly to examine not only intra-firm innovation processes but also inter-firm linkages and the structures of the public and private sector context within which innovation flourishes or can be persuaded to flourish and which are often seen as having spatial dimensions (Dodgsen & Rothwell 1994; Freeman 1974; Lundvall 1992; Nelson 1993)[1]. The translation of these theories about innovation into prediction and encouragement of particular location decisions by companies is complex: in Australia in the past it has often achieved a literally concrete manifestation in the provision of largely ineffective science and technology parks and "incubators" for new technology-based firms, despite poor experience worldwide with trying to create the conditions for a new "Silicon Valley".[2] Reliance on usually disappointing ventures of this kind suggests again that the use of a *series* of analytical lenses by policy-makers trying to affect enterprise location decisions gives a better overall picture and hence a greater chance of planning success than does the case of one alone. This is because each "lens" both highlights particular relevant characteristics of a given firm, group of firms or industry's activities and considers the particular relationships between local firms and the related institutions in a given geographical area, seen for analytical purposes as a local or regional element in a national system of innovation. Each "lens" highlights the role of different players and different relationships, thus indicating a variety of possible entry points to the production system for governments interested in promoting innovation as a means to urban economic development and particularly public authorities wishing to ensure a good match between firm decisions and broader questions of city development.

Some approaches to economic growth and firm development are economic in orientation and derive from the work of Schumpeter and the neo-Schumpeterians. Others take a more clearly sociological or political and organisational approach as seen, for instance, in the work of Weiss (1988) and Kristensen (1991). Some are attempts to learn from growth stimulants and patterns in the past (in particular this applies to the *clusters* approach as it appears in the work of Michael Porter and his team) and may also look at individual business strategy, while others are rather analytical tools which seek to uncover relationships between actors and institutions which are usually not detected or not given due weight by more traditional approaches. This is particularly the case of the *complexes* approach discussed last in this chapter, which gives

---

1   For the application of new growth theories to Australia see Dowrick 1992.
2   See Joseph 1990 on Australia and Chanaron J-J 1989 for French experience.

especial weight to public sector R&D as a source of competitive advantage and points to roles for governments. All three can take full account of changes in both physical technology and organisational strategies.

1   Clusters

In recent years the frequent geographical *clustering* of innovative activities has attracted much attention by policy makers and companies alike. This clustering, first recognised by Schumpeter, has been interpreted in different ways. Sometimes the focus is on the generation of groups of highly interrelated products where for example, each develops from and/or contributes to the development of others. As Debresson, for example, has pointed out in his discussion of the Canadian snowmobile development, much of the dynamic effect of innovation may come through this clustering rather than through the intrinsic value of a single innovation (Debresson 1989: 1) or new technology.

The reasons for the clustering of innovations are in part technical and in part organisational. The opening up of new technological frontiers affects the rate and directions of opportunities for innovation (Debresson 1989: 3). The cumulative nature of technical know-how encourages economies of scope through the transferability of learning benefits which enable shareable inputs to new products, notably at plant level. At an organisational level, the innovation process usually involves interaction between the user (innovator) and one or more suppliers (producers) and a longer-term productive relationship may increase clustering. This clustering may cross industry lines and in some areas has been successfully fostered by government (Debresson gives the example of the French *Train Grande Vitesse*). This approach thus focuses attention on innovation through the development of new and inter-related products, each building on the others.

A broader analysis of clusters in the national innovation process is provided by Porter (1990) in his book *The Competitive Advantage of Nations*. The question Porter wishes to answer is that of why only certain countries even in the West, generate many companies which become successful international competitors in one or more industries.

The analytical "lens" used by Porter to answer this question brings into focus the individual company and its place in the structure of a particular cluster of firms in the same industry. Competitive pressure and the associated continuous innovation provide, Porter suggests, the dynamic of the advantage which companies in this virtuous circle derive. The unit of analysis is the industry but Porter points out that most successful national industries comprise *groups of firms*, not isolated participants, and that *most leading international competitors are located in the same city or region.*

Porter suggests that the competitive advantage of continuously innovating firms in each area derives from their position within a national configuration of four sets of factors which he conceptualises as a "diamond". The "diamond" is in turn a function of four sets of conditions. These are: factor conditions — the nation's position in factors of production such as skilled labour, capital stock, knowledge resources or infrastructure; demand conditions — the nature of *home* demand in particular for a product or service; the presence of related and supporting industries that are also internationally competitive; local conditions governing how companies are created, organised and managed and the intensity of domestic rivalry.

As a system these elements create the context for firms' birth and growth. Porter believes that nations succeed in particular industries because their home environment is the most dynamic and the most challenging, stimulating firms to upgrade and widen their advantages over time and constituting a mutually reinforcing system.

When all the elements of the "diamond" are functioning satisfactorily the outcome is not one but a cluster of successful firms operating within and between given industries. These firms are mutually supporting. As Porter says:

> Benefits flow forward, backward and horizontally. Aggressive rivalry in one industry tends to spread to others in the cluster, through the exercise of bargaining power, spin-offs and related diversification. Entry from other industries within the cluster spurs upgrading by stimulating diversity in R&D approaches. . . Information flows freely and innovations diffuse rapidly through the conduits of suppliers or customers. . . Interconnections within the cluster . . . lead to new ways of competing and entirely new opportunities. (1990a: 151)

Porter's analysis focuses essentially on firms and their context but says little about two central elements of that environment which are central to this chapter. These are technological change and the role of government. Further, Porter's analysis only incidentally mentions the likely geographic propinquity of firms in successful clusters, although in practice they tend to be close by, and says little about the size of the firm involved. This stands in sharp contrast to the notion of "industrial district" first developed by Marshall (1961) and since much analysed by writers rediscovering the industrial districts of Italy, Germany, Japan and Denmark (Piore & Sabel 1984), where the links between companies are central.

The analyses of industrial districts focus on similar elements of competition to those outlined by Porter. In particular, they emphasise skilled and flexible labour and the stimulation of constant competition from other suppliers to the same market. In that competition *technological innovation* plays a crucial role. Analysts of industrial districts however, also emphasise the importance of *collaboration* between firms rather than the *competition*, albeit balanced by linkages of different kinds, that is at the forefront of Porter's analysis. *Geographical propinquity* is also an important element of the system, encouraging both information flows and collaboration and the innovation necessary to compete successfully with dynamic neighbouring firms. Firms in industrial districts are aided by government policies both at the infrastructural level (eg provision of excellent technical education in Denmark) and at the fiscal level (special taxation regimes for artisans and firms employing fewer than a specified number of workers as in Italy). Together these factors have encouraged the growth of firms by subdivision and division on an amoeba-like basis so that many small enterprises result rather than a few hierarchical ventures. The activity of such firms is central to the economic dynamism of many city and suburban zones, although perhaps less so in Australia than elsewhere.

This approach then leads us to consider the relationship between specific aspects of the public infrastructure available to firms, the governance of urban spaces and the economic activity that occurs there. In particular, policy-makers sometimes deduce that the encouragement of economic growth based on technological innovation by small or start-up firms (New Technology Based Firms (NTBFs)) requires provision of special spaces such as technology parks. While it is clear that NTBFs in some industries do cluster in some areas, this is by no means obviously the case everywhere, or the relationship between firms in areas of new technology and the clustering found may be indirect. As Saxenian (1991) has implied in a recent report on Silicon Valley, there may be periods when such assistance is vital but it may vary over time, clustering at some periods of company organisation and product development — being less vital than at others. In the early years of Silicon Valley encouragement to innovation, as well as provision of resources in the form of ready markets and skilled labour, came not from broader public policies for the development of urban areas but from government defence establishments, whereas now the essential collective infrastructure is more that of the region as a whole than of any specific establishments (Saxenian 1991: 276). The importance of the defence establishments in the pioneering days, however, suggests that urban policy makers need yet another "lens" for their analysis of the course of action most likely to create the desired innovation clustering effect. This second lens is outlined in the next section.

2   Chains

The images of pathways to successful innovation and growth provided by these analyses discussed above focus on the notion of *cluster* or groupings of firms in the same or a related industry and produce images which are *weblike*.

A contrasting image of a productive structure and its innovative capacity through technological and product change is that provided by analysis in terms of *chains* of production. These *chains of production* are composed of chains of interlinked companies which cut across the traditional boundaries of primary, secondary and tertiary activities and link companies through their contribution to the final product. Each chain appears in the analysis as a kind of *rib* where companies primarily link to those ahead and behind them in the productive process. The chain highlights the forward and backward linkages and can do so both for an industry and for a particular major product within it. This "lens" is perhaps most useful in the analysis of activity where key core firms assemble complex products and through them lead the development activities of the whole chain and also where large supplier firms similarly lead segments of the chain.

The lead company does not have to be a manufacturer, however. Senker's (1988) work on supermarkets in the United Kingdom and Greig's (1991, 1992) work on the clothing sector in Australia indicate clearly that technological and organisational innovation can be pushed through the whole chain by major retailers who force their manufacturing suppliers to upgrade their quality and manufacturing methods.

Governments anxious to find the most effective points of entry to productive systems which they believe to be in need of technological and organisational upgrading can use the chain of production analysis to find the weak points in the chain, to encourage the filling of gaps which are hindering the development of the whole chain or to put pressure on the lead firms to stimulate the desired changes further down the line. Once a series of companies in an industry changes to JIT or Total Quality Management (TQM) methods, reciprocal change in supplier firms is very likely to follow and lead to the upgrading not only of the whole chain but also of at least parts of related chains to which key suppliers

143

are linked through their other markets. Each chain is not a perfectly integrated whole and the degree of innovation "leakage" at each node can be established.

This approach sheds light on the likely effects of specific technological changes — including alterations on managerial practice — on economic activity in both small and larger city areas and indeed whole regions. Monitoring such technological changes using this "lens" is important to city planners for two reasons. The first is that the changes may generate major shifts in employment opportunities and financial flows. This can be seen very easily in the case of the auto industry in certain areas of Melbourne where so much money is spent by the vehicle assemblers with suppliers that any change in the supply structure of the kind usually associated with a shift to JIT management has far-reaching consequences (Marceau 1990b). While city planners are clearly already highly conscious of the employment effects of highly visible changes such as plant closures, the chains of analysis approach allows them to examine the effects of other aspects of company reorganisation in a much more sophisticated way and to develop new strategies to both minimise the external problems caused and encourage new entrepreneurial activity which can profit from the resources newly available and which may need help in the initial stages. This approach may assist governments with selecting among candidates for assistance with facilities, favourable loans, the provision of educational and other retraining schemes etc.

The same approach may also be used in designing stimulation of further economic activity in local city areas, for instance when considering the siting of major lead organisations. Such stimulatory activity requires coordination and cooperation between numerous public and private bodies. These include private sector producers, public and private sector users (firms and other organisations), the producers of the R&D which lies behind much technological change and productive innovation and government regulatory organisms.

In many cases, however, this more positive approach to the spatial capturing of the benefits of technological change, which is especially important in Australia with its concentrated population, to promote urban economic growth may be best served by using the third analytical "lens" outlined in the next section.

3   Complexes

The use of the notion of *complexes* to analyse productive activity and its further stimulation has been particularly developed by van Tulder and a group of colleagues from some of the small industrial countries of Europe and from Australia. The approach is particularly appropriate for small countries, including Australia, Glatz and van Tulder (1989) suggest, as it contains both concern for a strong welfare element as part of the analytical framework itself, thus playing on these countries' characteristic strengths, and a recognition of the finite resources available to such countries. Most important, it recognises the very considerable importance of *public* rather than private sector research in many small countries, notably Australia, the existence of only a relatively few key players in any area and therefore the importance of public authorities in encouraging innovation and technological advance.

It is also important as an analytical tool for use in devising public industry policies because, van Tulder (1988) and Glatz and van Tulder (1989) suggest, small industrial countries face a particular set of economic pressures. In particular, they face problems with: the globalisation of production in certain key industries and the dominance of large firms from large countries in crucial sectors of the international economic arena; their small home markets, especially for more specialised products; the small amounts of money available for R&D; their negligible international market power (they are price- and product-takers) and very limited margins for manoeuvre in public policy action. In addition they are being squeezed by the arrival on the scene of important new players acting in their traditional areas of operation.

The development of policies which have most chances of enabling small countries to maximise their chances of success — or at least to avoid peripheralisation — in the international restructuring race, van Tulder and Glatz suggest, requires yet another set of analytical lenses, different from those of clusters, industrial districts, chains of production or the "development block" approach of Dahmén (1988).

The approach proposed is that of focusing on *complexes* of activities. These complexes are conceptualised as formalised or informal networks of cooperation between four major groups of actors. These are:

1. producers (firms);
2. users (consumers, usually other firms);
3. public sector research organisations;
4. regulators (governments of all levels).

Analysing the functioning of selected complexes or potential complexes involves examining the ways in which these actors interact in given national, regional and local entities. Successful complexes are those where each actor or set of actors is working to the full extent possible with all the others. It is this productive interaction which constitutes the "development power" (to use Dahmén's 1988 phrase) of the complex and which can be the basis of supportive action by urban and regional authorities.

Any national economy, large or small, contains different kinds of complexes but in Australia most are concentrated in city areas. Some are old-established but declining and in need of renovation through technological and organisational change (eg the auto industry) advancement; some are in core fields, such as telecommunications, and can be the basis for new industries, offering major export markets; some are welfare-related and assured of continued high levels of public expenditure which can be used for development purposes; others are in emerging sectors and pose special challenges because they are at the leading edge of both private sector and government policy and there are few models elsewhere to guide investment. The task of urban managers is thus to identify which complexes are contributing most to the development of their cities and which complexes could be persuaded to operate more effectively in generating economic activity of benefit to the local urban as well as the national community. It is also their task to analyse strengths and weaknesses and to negotiate improvements through bargaining with the key players in both public and private sectors in the complex.

In the context of urban development policies perhaps the most important welfare complexes are those centred on public institutions such as universities and hospitals because these are essentially funded by the public purse and therefore subject to public decisions. Following analysis based on the *complexes* model, institutions such as hospitals which are now frequently seen simply as *black holes* of expenditure could be made to play a major role in local development strategies by local policies linking health and education spending to the capacity of local firms. They could do this for instance by instituting new pressures to encourage closer local user-producer relations and better-sited investment in public facilities and, above all, research nodes.

The *complexes* set of lenses has three major advantages over the other perspectives outlined in this chapter as both an analytical approach to the discussion of innovation and as a basis for public policy development in urban zones. The first is that it contains a specific role for government authorities which may act directly to assist the complex rather than being reduced to providing general infrastructure. The second is that it indicates the central importance of public R&D facilities, especially in small countries which have few R&D dollars and little investment in business R&D as is the case in Australia. Well-functioning complexes analysed using this four-cornered approach indicate successful ways in which such scarce funds can be used and suggest the importance of developing sophisticated government education and research policies aimed at encouraging the innovation increasingly necessary for economic development. In Australia this requires closer coordination between all levels of government. Thirdly and in particular, the approach allows the analyst to pinpoint weaknesses in the complex much more clearly and thus to devise more effective policies for plugging gaps. Thus, for example, it may be possible to boost the productivity and local economic development power of a complex dependent on a flow of considerable public funds, such as the health complex mentioned above, but currently "disorganised" or "malfunctioning" because the different actors are not maximising productive interactions and not focusing public resources on encouraging innovation. As with successful chains of production, many complexes need a lead organisation to provide the links necessary for rapid innovation across a broad range of activities.

IV   Conclusion

Encouraging such effective linkages is especially important in Australian cities which are usually the space in which major changes are occurring. The transformation of the productive system through deregulation of critical services and dismantling of protection was decided at federal level and is being continued, or accelerated in some cases, at State level. The Australian population is concentrated in a very few urban areas. It is therefore these *city* populations which are bearing the brunt of very considerable changes in patterns of production, distribution and employment. In Australia, State governments share responsibility with city managers of all levels for the positive reorganisation of cities and for palliating the negative effects of change. In the context of a broad shift to a new international — more global — system and especially of major shifts in the activity of productive organisations of our region, the technological transformations which are facilitating altered organisational forms have particular salience. When so much is volatile and uncertain, the analytical tools used for policy making by city managers need to be especially robust. Those that are suggested here are derived from leading edge international research in the field and when used appropriately constitute both analytical tools and chips for the successful bargaining with other actors needed to release local urban development power.

Finding the right structures for innovation and putting them together in effectively functioning systems which maximise the innovative capacity of either a country or a sub-unit such as a city, requires the analyst to view the productive structure through not one but a variety of different lenses. Each approach outlined in this chapter provides a partial view and brings to prominence certain aspects of the economic and socio-political structures concerned: none can analyse every aspect of the economy but each adds vital data on the organisational dynamics of the productive system and its transformation. Each is a necessary supplement to both the cruder neo-classical views of industrial competitiveness and the more simplistic recipes put forward by policy makers who too often try rather blindly to apply in Australian urban and industrial conditions the latest discovery of a policy success story overseas. In a properly functioning and effective national system of innovation analysis using any of these lenses should indicate particularly effective linkages between players in both public and private sectors, at a firm and organisational level and across crucial industry sectors.

Chapter 8

CITIES AS
TECHNOLOGY GENERATORS

Jim Falk

Over the past two decades it has become widely understood that technological change is a central policy issue for any nation which wishes to maintain or improve its economic position in an intensely competitive world. Historically, the industrialisation which generates technological change and urbanisation have gone hand in hand. Yet the relationship between cities and strategies for technological change has received surprisingly little attention.

Globally, cities are areas of growth. Over the past 40 years the world's urban population has grown at four per cent per annum, adding some 40-50 millions of people per year, and raising the total number of people living in cities from 300 million to some 1.3 billion (International Bank for Reconstruction and Development 1991: 4).

According to The International Bank for Reconstruction:

> Rapid demographic growth will add 600 million people to cities and towns in developing countries during the 1990s, about two-thirds of the expected population increase. Of the world's 21 megacities, which will expand to have more than 10 million people, 17 will be in developing countries. With urban economic activities making up an increasing share of GDP in all countries, the productivity of the urban economy will heavily influence economic growth. (1991: 4)

In total, by the end of this century, over half the world's population is expected to live in cities (World Commission on Environment and Development 1987: 8). In Australia, it has been estimated, some 90 per cent of GDP is created in cities, and more than half in the capital cities.

Given the current and potentially even greater future significance of cities it is surprising how often they are treated as peripheral in key areas of policy. Thus for example, in Australia, key preoccupations of Australian policy — employment, competitivity, equity, economic growth, health and environmental sustainability — are seldom considered in close association with the dynamics of the city. The policy focus tends to be shaped according to the demarcations of government jurisdictions, in particular the nation, or in the Australian federal system, the nation and the States. Also, in Australia as in many other places, the frequent organisation of the city through a collection of local governments responsible for the various localities tends to further fragment the image of cities and limit the ways in which their potential roles are understood and utilised.

Thus, although cities are big communities and increasingly large proportions of the population live in them, the picture of these as communities is fractured and eroded by both closer and more extended systems of organisation which shape people's daily lives. Thus while cities constitute much of the infrastructure of everyday life, our political and policy language continues to parcel the world into the national community on the one hand, and the micro community of family, friends and "local" organisation on the other. The result is that cities are seldom conceived or structured as either effective communities or politically significant actors.

I   The Changing Context

The emphasis of much of the past discussion of technological change on national policy, national strategies, and the development of the national economy is a common feature of political analysis. Its roots go back more than a century, to a model of a world conceptualised as the sum of a set of discrete and sovereign nation states.

This old tidy picture, as I have argued elsewhere, is an increasingly poor explanation of how the contemporary world really works (Camilleri & Falk, 1992). In particular, the central precept — that national governments can be "sovereign" — with supreme authority over all that happens within their territorial domains — is increasingly challenged by many changes in the global political economy.

1.   First, the central theme of industrial development of the previous century — its emphasis on an increasing scale of organisation — has continued beyond national boundaries. One early result of increasing organisational size was the growth of

the role of national government instrumentalities (and the corresponding reduction in power of regional administrations). However, the trend has taken us well beyond that. Thus, we see the emergence of larger multinational regions (such as the European Community), the increasing size and scope of transnational corporations, the increasing visibility of what is now understood to be global production and communication systems, and indeed the emergence of a global market. In all of these developments large scale organisation plays an ever more important and overt role.

2. Second, technology (nuclear weapons, acid rain, communications technology, money and information flows, and much else) also cuts across national boundaries. Frequently the outcome is as much national policy being reshaped to accommodate the requirements of the transnational technical systems, as the national government shaping the technology.

3. Third, production systems have become integrated at a global level — it no longer means much to talk about "our" products or "their" products.

4. Fourth, and perhaps most importantly, governments now find themselves one of many actors in what is increasingly a single, integrated world market. In it they compete with other actors (for example, transnational corporations), some of which have equivalent, or greater, economic power.

The result is a world which is increasingly poorly described by the tidy sovereignty model, but is instead characterised by "shifting allegiances, new forms of identity and overlapping tiers of jurisdiction" (Camilleri & Falk 1992: 256).

From the above perspective, the role of the nation state is becoming progressively less privileged and dominant at the very time that the city is emerging as a larger and potentially increasingly important centre of human activity. The point here needs to be clearly stated. It is *not* that, as the claim of national governments to sovereignty is undermined, cities (or any other particular structure or community) could emerge in their place as sovereign entities. Rather it is that in a time of rapid transition in which the old model of sovereignty is losing explanatory power, the meaning, form and structure of civil society is itself becoming open to renegotiation.

The issue of what are the central political communities and how they operate is thus facing challenge. There is the possibility that some communities which are in a state of rapid growth (whether localities, cities or regions) can be reconceptualised — that they can be brought into sharper focus as stronger and more effective social, economic and political actors. Cities, with large and rapidly increasing populations and economic activity, may be particularly promising in this respect. That is however just a possibility. Whether or not it is realised will depend, in part, upon the strategies that corresponding communities adopt and implement.

II   Competitiveness in Context

One response to the decrease in the dominance of the nation state as *the* locus of political intervention is to seek means to develop effective technology and innovation policies which can regulate activity *beyond* the boundaries of the nation. As Soete argues:

> [T]here is now an urgent need for international policy making in this area. The need for international competition policy arises from national differences in competition policy and the absence of an international regime for overseeing transnational investment, acquisitions and mergers. Such policy should aim at counter-acting the emergence of world wide cartels between global firms; reduce the divergence between national competition policies, and monitor more closely the degree and extent of globalisation of multi-domestic firms. (1991: 60)

There is much to be done at this level. But whilst policy and international political organisation continues to be formulated within the *sovereignty discourse*, it will tend to focus more on providing the regulational environment, infrastructure and strategies which will develop competitive advantage for state or nation.

One problem with this, as Michael Porter, in his study of national competitivity, stresses is that:

> [T]here is still no persuasive theory of national competitiveness. What is more, there is not even an accepted definition of the term "competitiveness" as applied to a nation. While the notion of a competitive company is clear, the notion of a competitive nation is not. (1990b: 75)

The concept of competitivity derives from the theory of the firm. But the nation is a much more complex and diffuse social system constituting, as Benedict Anderson (1983) notes, an imagined community of diverse and contradictory interests. It is, therefore, not surprising that most of the relevant theoretical development has continued to concentrate at the level of the firm. It is outside the scope of this chapter to review the relevant literature.[1] It is sufficient to stress that

---

1   A good review can be found in Jane Marceau (1990a), in particular p. 16.

in a world in which communication and transport is increasingly efficient and cheap, the issues associated with national borders become, increasingly, only one factor in investment decisions. Rather than seeing the world as a set of nations it is possible to view the world as a chess board of regions in which various parts of the *chain of production* of any given commodity or set of commodities, may be located according to the particular characteristics and attractions of that region.

The recent literature on the strategies of firms tends to reflect this view of reality. In particular, amongst the many issues raised in this work, it is worth noting that:

1. No country is competitive in every or even most industries and there are striking differences in the patterns of competitiveness in every country (Porter 1990b: 74).

2. Firms achieve their competitive advantage through acts of innovation. These involve the development of new technologies, new products, and new organisational structures. Innovation may occur anywhere along the chain of production. It may, and often does include new relationships with other companies and aspects of the firm's environment. Since no firm can do everything in the most efficient way, especially on a global scale, collaboration between firms in strategic alliances and other partnerships is an increasingly obvious feature of the strategy of many successfully innovative firms.

3. According to Porter, innovation thus responds to a "diamond" of factors which includes, for any given firm, the factor conditions, nature of the local demand, the presence of related and supporting industries, and the conditions governing how companies are created and organised and the rivalries that they face. Porter notes:

    > Two elements, domestic rivalry and geographic concentration have especially great power to transform the diamond into a system – domestic rivalry because it promotes improvement in all the other determinants and geographic concentration because it elevates and magnifies the interaction of the four separate influences. (1990b: 83)

It is therefore not surprising that competitive productive firms tend to cluster their activities within regions. Compatible with this, much recent theory stresses the importance of the characteristics of the overall social, technical and economic environment, not so much of the nation as of the region in which firms develop and cluster (Soete 1991). Not infrequently, those clusters are both supported by, and support a growing urban infrastructure.

III   Cities and Innovation

Over the past decade considerable attention has been paid to the idea of nation-wide strategies to foster the development of national systems of innovation. Here attention is paid to developing combined systems of infrastructure and companion industries which will enable continued development of at least some vigorously innovative and highly productive industry. This emphasis, which is consistent with the discourse of national sovereignty, tends to marginalise the possible importance of other systems which either transcend or are embedded within the nation. In particular, with this emphasis on firm and nation, cities tend to be given a low profile (Ergas 1987; Freeman & Lundvall 1988; Porter 1990a, 1990b).

The history of economic analysis helps reinforce this tendency. Whilst, as Krugman (1991: 483) notes, there has been a tradition of modelling descending from von Thunen applied to urban studies, it is fair to say that "The study of economic geography — of the location of factors of production in space — occupies a relatively small part of standard economic analysis" and "[P]lays at best a marginal role in economic theory."

But cities are where most of the market resides and where most of the productive activity takes place. Generally speaking, they are where firms cluster and constitute the infrastructure upon which the firms draw. Indeed, the city (or municipality) may well form the more natural and useful geographical social and economic region in which to understand and plan for the facilitation and shaping of desired interlinkages.

This perspective is supported by Jacobs (1985) who argues that economic policies are wrongly geared to the nation state rather than to the city. She notes that from Antiquity, through the Renaissance and to the present, cities have contributed much of what we consider to be prosperity (as suggested by our use of the terms "urbane" and "civilised"). Jacobs goes on to argue, using innumerable examples, that this preoccupation with the national in policy theory and practice results in societies in decline being unable to rescue themselves and those trying to advance missing the problems and opportunities that exist.

Jacob's claims about the primacy of cities as economic entities in their maintenance of the economic viability of nations may remain controversial. It is sufficient here to take her analysis as further support for the contention that cities and their economies have been excessively marginalised from both economic analysis, and the development of frameworks for determining innovation policy.

The *reasons* why firms tend to localise their activities within cities has received some attention. One factor, as developed by Myrdal (1957), is the "circular causation" relationship between the agglomeration of manufacturers around large markets and the growth of large markets where there are agglomerations of manufacturers. This relationship has been recently explored through economic modelling (Krugman 1991).

In addition, there is a considerable and longstanding literature which points to the external benefits to industries of a large pool of workers with the necessary range of skills, the importance of the availability (through the presence of compatible industries in the vicinity) of non-tradeable specialised inputs, and the value to industries of operating in a milieu in which information about technological possibilities and market trends and options is readily available (Hoover 1948).

From this and the underlying innovation literature, it may be possible to begin to develop analyses of the aspects of cities which would encourage the growth of industry within them and then *strategies* for strengthening them.

One such feature which has received attention is the role of cities in facilitating the informal transfer of knowledge between industries. Thus, for example, Romer (1992) and Lucas (1988) argue in particular that cities provide the geographical proximity through which ideas and "knowledge spillovers" are easily transmitted between firms acting as an "engine of growth". There is still debate however on central issues (such as whether local monopoly (Arrow 1962; Romer 1992) or local competition (Porter 1990a, 1990b) favours the stimulation of innovation, and whether the most important knowledge transfers come from within or outside a core industry (Glaeser et al 1991).

The literature attests to the need for more analysis. It does not yet provide a rigorous menu of prescriptions for the strategic advancement of innovation at the city level. However, since the same may be said of the literature on national innovation this should not deter us from noting that a range of reasonable suggestions have been made as to the way in which the organisation of cities can assist the innovation process.

Some of these are dealt with in more detail elsewhere in this book. Thus, for example, the role of cities as markets (Greig Chapter 5), as communication systems (Lamberton Chapter 4, Marceau Chapter 7), and as systems of supporting infrastructure (Brindle Chapter 2) has already been examined. Similarly, we may note that cities provide the pools of varied skills, the potential for clustering of companion industries, the efficient integration of their inputs and outputs (including what might otherwise be rejected as wastes), the diversity of industrial capability required for the rapid formation of effective strategic alliances, and the ready availability of a market, and feedback from consumers which can drive the invention, testing and early development of marketing strategies required for effective innovation.

IV Cities and Innovation Strategy

The above suggests that there would be virtue in paying more attention to the role of cities in innovation. Beyond that it would be useful (but harder) to devise strategies to achieve more effective innovation in the urban context.

One superficially attractive possibility is to artificially create cities designed to foster fruitful interactions between targeted industry sectors and related firms. However, as discussed also by Lamberton (Chapter 4) and Droege (Chapter 9), the existing history of technology parks and artificial cities such as the Multifunction Polis (MFP) (to be built near Adelaide, Australia), and similar projects which have too frequently become white elephants, attests to the difficulties of transforming the visions of success into reality.

A study of technology parks in the United States has found that they fail, at least on the criteria of the study, on average at least half the time. A study of parks founded during the 1960s showed that they often suffered from poor profit performance, let alone contributing to the job creation and regeneration of the local economy which invariably features strongly in the justification of public support for the initiatives. The criteria of *success* have often proved to be conveniently flexible (Joseph 1986).

Further, where technology parks have been widely accepted as successful (for example, Silicon Valley or the Cambridge Technology Park), many studies attribute the growth of the park to existing clustered high technology, rather than the park being its cause (Joseph 1987: 193). It seems likely that the disappointing performance of the technology park strategy is precisely because, for the strategy to be successful, it would have to anticipate and provide the necessary complex web of circumstances, rather than relying on it somehow arising organically around firms, which would innovate and prosper, in supposedly natural clusters (Camilleri et al 1991).

In many ways, the proposed Multi-function Polis represents just such a strategy writ large — in this case the creation of an entire small city built around design criteria which are intended to attract substantial foreign investment in technological innovation. The MFP proposal has gone through a remarkable series of rhetorical shifts as the interests supporting it have attempted to adjust both to criticism, and to ground their vision more clearly in terms of economic, social and political feasibility. It is likely we have not yet reached the end of this process. It is however still useful to note that at various stages in this proposal it aimed to:

1. build a series of centres (eg Environmental Management, and MFP University, Aquatic Toxicology, Institute for Language and Culture, an Information Utility) from existing strengths in the existing city of Adelaide;

2. create some of the original Ministry of International Trade and Industry (MITI) (Japan) concepts of a futuristic city in which residential and industrial activities are blended seamlessly;

3. merge environmental sustainability with foreign investment attraction in the development of a range of high-technology industries;

4. integrate a large and presumably transient international corporate population into a well formed and effective city community; and

5. utilise a highly deregulated environment (to attract investment) but at the same time adequate regulation to prevent the development of social and economic inequities, preserve democratic norms, and maintain a sense of community in a highly commercialised environment.

Given the dearth of economic analysis in the proposal, its failure to define the economic structure of the city, its likely impact on the surrounds of Adelaide, South Australia, or Australia, the uncertainty about the compatibility of its various objectives, and a lack of detail about how they are to be achieved, it is difficult to assess the likely success of the project.[2] One is, however, entitled to some scepticism towards the realisability of the various aims that have been enunciated, especially given the failure to examine how the complex and subtle chains of interactions and alliances, which organically develop within successful industrial clusters, are to be created here. As others have pointed out, the history of Japanese experiments in the creation of such cities does not augur particularly well (James 1990).

---

2   For a detailed critique of the MFP-Adelaide feasibility study see Camilleri et al (1991).

As a general guide it seems likely that if urban strategy is to go beyond this it is most likely to be successful if directed at developing policies for the improvement of existing, viable cities, rather than at developing ambitious projects to construct what are effectively new ones. If cities are to be shaped as technology generators this means simultaneously developing a wide spectrum of urban strengths. The possibilities of future technological generation must therefore be assessed in the light of a realistic assessment of a city's existing and potential strengths. (This was in fact more the character of the Sydney proposal for the MFP (New South Wales 1990) which was based more on the development of strengths within the existing metropolis than developing a separate new city.)

Probably partly because of the complexity of the issues to be faced, and also because of the restricted powers of many city administrations (especially in Australia) attempts at development policies in cities are generally quite restricted, concentrating on the provision of urban development action grants, industrial development bonds, business assistance centres, advertising and promotion campaigns, and rate and other regulational measures (Clingermayer et al 1990).

If we are to go beyond this, without falling into the traps presented by the MFP, then we will need to develop urban innovation strategy which takes full account of the organic nature of cities. This requires not only a careful examination of the virtues of a particular city, but also a more global analysis of the ways in which differences between cities can play an important role. One aspect of this is the way in which different cities are not only capable in different areas of innovation, but the different ways their communities may judge what in any case is a desirable innovation.

1   Cities and innovation objectives

So far we have treated innovation as a single, unexamined category. This simply follows the dominant tendency to equate innovation with economic growth and to isolate economic growth as the central and determining requirement of national policy.

This tendency in policy is a reflection of the situation of national and State governments which find themselves steadily less able to challenge the dominating and shaping forces of an integrated world market. As a result, rather than trying to steer the direction of the nation, governments attempt to surf more agilely in the direction the global economic currents and waves seem already to be moving. In this race, the contest is not so much over the direction to be taken as over the attempt to gain a slight advantage over others with whom they compete. Within this framework, rigidly confined by the boundaries of economic determinism, innovation strategy is simply conceived of as a tool for achieving economic growth. It is possible, however, to consider innovation strategy in a less confined perspective, as a tool for meeting broader social goals.

Although innovation has frequently become uncritically equated with public good, this equation should not be assumed. Innovation and its role in economic growth is good only if the net changes resonate with community values and advance towards community goals. Clearly community preferences will vary with cultural mores. And cultural differences, and thus community goals, may well differ not only between national communities, but may differ, at times perhaps even more, between city communities. In short:

1. City culture, expectations and values will all be germane to a city's capacity for supporting particular areas of technological innovation.

2. Different expectations and values may well result in different community goals for innovation.

3. Different political and administrative structures may express these goals in different ways and with different levels of effectiveness.

4. The goals that develop, and the way they are expressed within a city will be relevant to the innovation it can effectively support.

5. The pattern of urban regulation itself is an important example. It will help shape what is encouraged in innovation and what directions are likely to be fruitful.

It is also an excessive simplification to treat "the city" as a single unproblematic formation. As Jacobs notes, the dynamics of cities reach beyond the formal city borders often transforming much larger regions in which they are embedded. Hong Kong provides a particularly striking example of this, but there are many others. For many cities (for example, Sydney, Australia) the formal jurisdiction of the city (the "City of Sydney") encompasses little more than the central business district, an area trivial in comparison to the extent of the metropolis as a whole. Even where city-wide "metro" administrations are in place, their jurisdictional boundaries often encompass less than half the inhabitants of what might reasonably be considered the city (Brisbane, Australia provides an illustrative example).

What about [?] part.
Too contat [?]

It is important to note, therefore, that the central argument here should not focus solely on the city, let alone on all cities. What *is* asserted here is that we are at a time of transition, when the traditional centre of political power and authority (the nation state) is finding its dominance undermined through the emergence of a more complex transnational world of shifting allegiances, new forms of identity and overlapping tiers of jurisdiction. It is also a time of rapid innovation, and the processes of innovation increasingly depart from the scale of the national domain. In this situation, there is the possibility that some communities which are in a state of rapid growth (whether localities, cities or regions) can be brought into sharper focus and play a stronger and more effective than previous social, economic and political role in the shaping of that process of innovation in the direction of *their* long-term aspirations.

Of course, not all cities fit this description. Depending not only on economic and physical features, but also on the history of political and social structures, attitudes and habits, in some localities it may be whole regions, or alternatively communities within cities which may be identified as most effectively achieving the objective. It would require more space than this chapter allows to identify, on a case by case basis, which regions, cities or localities may have the appropriate characteristics. Here it is sufficient to note that there is a large number of cities which are both rapidly growing and provide promising infrastructure for innovation. At least *a priori*, these are places which support communities which may, by the conscious formulation of desired directions and the implementation of appropriate innovation policies, be able to play a stronger role in shaping innovation to meet their goals.

2   Environmental innovation as an example

Environmental innovation provides an illuminating example of the way in which cities, innovation goals, and innovation strategies could fruitfully combine.

The growth of mainstream environmental concern reflects a divergence between the general direction of innovation and economic development in Western societies, and community values. Globally, human activity, directed at economic growth, is resulting in the extermination of some 7000 species per year — more than 1000 times the natural rate (Kellogg & Bretherton 1986); has trebled the amount of material moved annually by all rivers to the oceans (Holgate et al 1982);

has raised the radioactivity in the seas by one per cent; [3] is utilising some 60,000 chemicals, many of which are foreign to the lungs, kidneys and other organs of human beings, and more generally the biosphere; and is increasing the usage of these chemicals by 1500 annually (Holgate et al 1983: 296). Human activity has ruptured the fragile ozone layer, which screens the global ecosystem from the damaging effects of short wavelength ultraviolet radiation, and is changing the equilibrium balance of atmospheric gases, threatening to alter the earth's mean temperature with potentially serious future climatic consequences.[4]

The positive virtue of the market as the central mechanism for generating wealth, thus carries as an underside its equally central role in generating unsustainability. Two of the contributing factors which are usually noted are the facts that:

1. future generations in principle cannot bid in today's markets. Consequently the market may well underemphasise the virtues of sustainability; and

2. the market provides no direct cost to many human activities which nevertheless dramatically damage the environment (for example, emitting carbon dioxide to the atmosphere). As a result, the pure reliance on the market poses grave challenges, to the integrity of both regional environments and ultimately the planetary biosphere, of which we are a part, and on which we depend for our survival (Falk & Brownlow 1989: 162-71).

As a consequence, it is only by intervention, and very probably significant intervention at that, that the road to sustainability may be able to be laid out and traversed.

It is however incorrect to suggest that practical action taken to meet the consequences of this market failure must automatically result in less economic growth. Rather, the choice by a particular community to emphasise environmental goals may well provide a basis for a highly effective innovation strategy.

Globally we are also now witnessing the rapid growth of a complex of environmental industries. The Organisation for Economic Cooperation and Development (OECD) (1991a, 1991b) has estimated that the research and development done by these industries amounts to some $10 billion annually. (Some 80 per cent of this research and development is funded by firms.) The total size of the industry is

---

3 Preston (in Goldberg 1977:799-815) calculates the total artificial radioactivity in the sea in 1970 at about 10^9 Ci compared with the natural level of K^{40} of $5 \cdot 10^{11}$ Ci.

4 See for example, Falk and Brownlow (1989:162-71) and references contained therein.

currently estimated at $185 billion and the OECD projects that this will rise to $300 billion by the end of this decade.

Of this environmental industry some 75 per cent of its output is currently in the form of equipment for environmental purposes (primarily end of pipe pollution abatement — water and effluent 29 per cent, waste management 21 per cent, air quality 15 per cent, other 11 per cent). Environmental services comprise a further 24 per cent of the output. Clearly this multi-billion dollar enterprise constitutes a new constituency of interest in environmental problems and promises the development of novel alliances for technological innovation for environmental improvement.

The growth of the environmental market thus represents a significant economic opportunity. It needs to be stressed, however, that the grasping of this opportunity is by no means inevitable. Only some communities will be able to take the lead. Communities which are sensitive to environmental concerns are likely to be well placed to provide the necessary markets and concentrations of skills, knowledge and companion industries which are appropriate to rapid development in this direction.

Australia has achieved an international reputation for concern about the environment, although it is far from clear that this reputation is well deserved. This reputation has developed partly in response to the Prime Minister's Statement on the Environment in July 1989 (which was itself, of course, a response to the dramatically increasing political concern in the Australian community about the environment), the development of an agreement between the States and the Commonwealth to work together to tackle problems of the environment, the early setting of Greenhouse Emissions Reductions targets by all States and the Commonwealth, and the production of a range of reports of varying quality and value produced from the various working groups of the ecologically sustainable development (ESD) Process.

All this has been matched by a comparable level of activity by Australian diplomats in the international arena. Yet little of this has focused on the changes which would be necessary to cities and in cities to achieve the necessary changes. For example, in the ESD process, cities appear only tacked on as an "intersectoral" issue, to be considered outside the main areas of mining, agriculture, forests, manufacturing, tourism, fisheries, energy production and use, and transport.

Cities, in their own right, have thus played a remarkably low key role in discussions of sustainability in Australia. A great deal of attention has been paid to wilderness, soil conservation, and the role of governments and citizens in preserving them. Great concern has been expressed about climate change, and innumerable conflicts have flared over issues of industrial pollution and resource usage — whether it be uranium mining or intractable waste dumps. But in all this, little attention has been paid to cities as a whole.

Cities, however, do play a central role in the *generation* of the environmental problems which confront us. The current direction of city development, especially in Australia, is starkly unsustainable. As a symptom we see the notorious process of urban sprawl, with the continuous migration of people to the outer rim of an expanding doughnut. We see the declining usefulness of the densely built up core of the inner city. We see the extraordinary pressures on everything from roads to energy supply, to the supply of entertainment, across the ever expanding expanse of the super metropolises. And we see the cities increasingly gobbling up the most arable and robust land in what is a large, but generally ecologically extremely vulnerable continent.

Cities are thus not just the sites at which economic activities are located which produce many of the ecological problems. The very form of cities contributes greatly to the enhancement of those problems.

For example, the distribution of activities and infrastructure, and the corresponding transport patterns in Australian cities have crucial implications for the levels of anthropogenic carbon dioxide emitted from Australia (Newman 1991). Similarly, the mechanisms within cities and the ways they are organised contribute greatly to their encroachment upon some of the most fertile areas of the generally fragile Australian ecosystem, their emission of ever greater volumes of pollutants, and their consumption of ever increasing quantities of resources. The quality of urban life, the values and habits of city communities, and the economic and political arrangements within them all interplay with the pattern of generation of unsustainability.

From the point of view of environmental innovation, environmental problems may be assets, but this is only true if there is a strong community commitment to resolving them.

V   The Importance of Community

The above suggests, at least *a priori*, that cities with a significant spectrum of environmental problems, with strong concerns about the environment, with a preparedness to invest in environmental innovation, and with regulational structures which give the use of that innovation a strong market have the potential to play a strong role in driving environmental innovation. This reinforces the observation that if there is to be a clear formulation of objectives, the enunciation of an urban strategy to achieve them, and the committed implementation of that strategy then this is most likely in a city with a strong sense of community, and the appropriate mechanisms in place to give it expression.

It would be fair to say that in Australia, despite their dominant role as the home of most Australians, cities are poorly equipped to meet the above requirement. Consider Sydney and Melbourne where many Australians live. Compared to the vast area of Australia these represent tightly packed communities, tied together by sophisticated city-wide mass communication channels, telecommunication systems, roads, and sharing entertainments, newspapers, and mutually affected by many environmental, economic and other issues. Yet few, if any, statistics are provided about inputs and outputs into these cities, the shaping of their affairs is on the one hand fractured into many local municipal governments with weak power. Much of the decision-making in the city is shaped by the more remote State, national and even international authorities.

The above must be qualified by the reality that interests in Melbourne and Sydney often dominate decision-making at the State level. The point is not that this is so, but that the community of those, and other cities, feels remarkably powerless to plan and shape the future of that community. Rather, the shaping and even the shape of the city appears as a remote and intangible issue, well beyond the grasp of the city community. This conclusion may be illustrated by focusing on the case of Sydney.

The population of Sydney represents close on one fifth of the Australian population. But, ironically, this large section of the national population seems disempowered in the face of not merely global but Australia and even city-wide environmental problems. There has been some welcome progress towards the development of city plans (the latest being "Metro 2000"), but the process has been extremely slow and difficult, the planning is still far from adequate, and the sense of a city-wide community undeveloped. So marginal is the conceptualisation of the city in Australian affairs that it does not even form a natural statistical district in most Australian statistical reporting. As a consequence it is not currently possible for citizens of Sydney, for example, to know how much energy their city is using, how much toxic gas they are producing, what the trends are in Sydney's resource consumption and pollution, or even how the city economy is developing and changing.

Current greenhouse research tends to concentrate on projected national and regional impacts of, and current and future national and

State contributions to greenhouse emissions. Strategies for change are usually cast in grand macroscopic goals at the national and State level. But how this could, should, or credibly might translate to the cities, where the overwhelming majority of Australians live, and most of the greenhouse emissions are generated, still remains largely unstudied.

Given these factors it is not surprising that the actual identification of the city and its activities provides a central challenge for reinforcing the potential constructive role of the city community. Techniques must often be developed for either directly or indirectly identifying flows of energy, investment, greenhouse emissions and much else through the city. Further, many activities within cities depend vitally on activities outside, or produce significant impacts beyond their boundaries. Thus the analysis of greenhouse emissions from a city requires the construction of matrices of both direct and indirect resource uses, and greenhouse gas outputs by sector. Similar problems are created in following investment flows into greenhouse emissive industries in cities. However, we need not reinvent the wheel. Possible starting points are already available from existing economic input-output analysis (Falk & Brownlow 1989: Appendix 3) and energy accounting techniques (Chapman 1974) for providing an economic and environmental statistical base which could help define a sharper picture of the activity and its implications of the city community.

VI   Making the Most of Cities

Consideration of the environmental example thus demonstrates the close interconnection between the role of the community, the setting of innovation objectives, and the effective implementation of strategies to meet them. For cities, as generators of innovation, two conclusions are suggested:

1   Strengthening community

The current fragmented structure of Australian cities leaves little sense of cohesive community and a weak form of local government. The result is that, apart from NIMBY ("Not In My Back Yard") responses, there is usually little initiative from the city community itself in shaping its own future. This suggests that a serious reconsideration of the powers of local government, as well as policy measures which will encourage local government and the community to which it is responsible, to act more deliberately, would be a valuable part of a strategy which could maximally utilise the city community in the development of its innovation potential. Policy and mechanisms to involve the breadth of organisation and communities within the broad ambit of the city in setting goals, planning and monitoring its implementation could play a role in strengthening the sense of an empowered city community which would be necessary for that community to realise more of its potential to shape the path of innovation which it will move along.

2   Utilising difference

If relevant cities are to be strengthened as social and administrative entities then a likely result is to bring into starker relief the differences between the cultures, objectives, strategies, successes and failures of different cities. In conjunction with other colleagues (Falk et al 1992), I have argued elsewhere that this is an important virtue from the point of view of encouraging innovation. In particular, to the extent that it makes strategies and their outcomes visible, it has the potential to increase the effectiveness of the "policy market".

The suggestion here is that in the same way that firms benefit from informal knowledge spill-overs between themselves and other firms (whether collaborators or competitors) cities may also benefit from knowledge of the success or failure of policy initiatives towards common objectives.

This concept of what has been called a "prototypes strategy" has also been discussed elsewhere.[5] The aims of such a strategy are:

1.   to characterise the potential for meeting different objectives within particular cities;

2.   to analyse the relationship between initiatives within cities and the State, national and international context within which they must be developed;

3.   to show by example the success and failure of different types of initiatives; and

4.   to strengthen the ability of city communities to intervene in the shaping of their activities towards commonly held objectives.

The strategy consists of forming agreements between a funding body and particular cities or municipalities for that community to implement certain strategies towards certain objectives, based upon clearly stated

---

5   The project was carried out in conjunction with the Centre for Technology, Environment and Development (CENTED) and the Centre for Global Urban Studies at Clark University, Worcester, Mass, USA; the Institute for Resource and Security Studies, Cambridge, Mass, USA; and the Centre for Energy, Environment and Technology, Administrative Staff College of India, Hyderabad, India.

and measurable targets. (In our case study these related to reducing greenhouse emissions at the city level.) A support group works with the community to monitor and analyse successes and failures and the reasons they occur. The support group will also provide information about relevant initiatives from other prototype cities. The support group also has the responsibility of collating and widely disseminating the results of the process. In this way a process of "grounded research, policy development and action" should produce an evolving series of success stories (at best) and cautionary tales (at worst). Either way, it should contribute greatly to the formulation of effective policy by allowing the organic processes in the city to interact dynamically with a disaggregated policy formation process.

One example would be to use national funds to encourage particular cities to bid in a competition to contract for the creation of "green zones". In these zones activity could be directed towards meeting a range of environmental sustainability criteria (and possibly other criteria such as work practices, industrial democracy, worker safety, training, work contracts). For example, a green zone in Sydney might encompass existing universities working on renewable energy and energy efficiency technology, firms working in the development and sale of these technologies, surrounding municipal councils developing strategies for more energy efficient developments within their locality and linked companies providing the services necessary to implement the plans. By learning from the success or failure of the various initiatives other city communities could be assisted in their development of innovation directed towards similar objectives.

In 1991, the then Minister for Health, Housing and Community Services, Mr. Brian Howe announced a substantial $800 million "Better Cities" program. Whilst it was not on that occasion utilised in the way described above, there seems to be no reason why, in future, a similar program could not be directed to developing urban innovation prototypes.

This process of strengthening the "policy market" in this way at the scale of cities would seem to have great potential. For example, it seems in principle that it could be utilised to contract with communities to improve the attractiveness of central regions sufficiently to encourage population movement back into the city centres, to develop more sustainable uses of energy through the city economy, to develop the statistical base necessary for the community to strive for greenhouse targets, and much more. There is no reason why the policies developed should not also be deliberately directed at strengthening the potential for corresponding innovation.

VII Conclusion

In principle, the more rapidly developing cities may well have increasingly greater potential to develop effective innovation strategies, and innovation strategies have a corresponding potential for making cities more effective and satisfying places to live. However, much of this potential remains to be utilised. The discussion in this chapter suggests rather than attempting to construct artificial cities equipped with infrastructure to support targeted industries, it may be more effective to strengthen those characteristics of existing cities which are conducive to innovation.

At the level of the city it is naive to simply aim for innovation. Different cities will have different cultures, values, capabilities, and objectives. And in response to these they will choose varying strategies with varying effect.

One central step towards utilising this difference would seem to be to take steps to further consolidate social cohesion by developing citywide mechanisms which enable cities to express these differences. A second step, would be to encourage cities to learn from each other through deliberate processes of competition and knowledge sharing towards common goals.

In this sense, innovation strategy is not just a project for the national state, but for regional State structures and city administrations themselves. It involves a reconsideration of what is done at these levels and the possibility of greatly strengthening the decision-making at the level of the city and the strategic relations between cities. And innovation is not a goal in itself. A wide range of public policy objectives relate to the direction in which innovation should grow. These relate to the integrity of the environment, quality of life, and the future shape and function of cities. The analysis in this chapter suggests that whether enunciated internationally, nationally or locally, at least some cities have a far greater potential role to play in developing the innovation required to meet these goals than is often suggested either in theory or in practice.

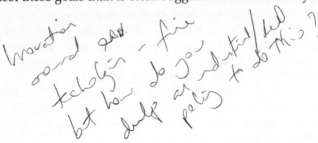

Chapter 9

TOMORROW'S METROPOLIS – VIRTUALISATION TAKES COMMAND: Technology, institutions, policy and design in the information age

Peter Droege

I Cities in an Advanced Technology Mood: A Visit to the Information City

The computer has seduced us into seeing the world from an information point of view, whether we think of science, society or life itself. Rightly or wrongly, the twin notion of information and information processing has become a major paradigm in thinking about the world. It is only natural that we try to understand cities in this way as well. Many urban qualities have been profoundly altered with the spread of thinking machines and modern communications. These changes have no easy explanations, and there is lots to be explored. To provide a general map for such expeditions, let us take a tour through cities from such an information-oriented viewpoint. This tour we might call, for simplicity's sake, a visit to the information city. The information city is a curious and complex kind of town, a place of concepts. Here, notions about cities mingle with ideas about information and communication, and the changing technologies we use to manipulate both.

On our walk, we will see four information city attractions. Like all good tourists, we will first take a look at ancient monuments, and how techniques of information handling are historically layered in cities. Along the way, we will stop at the new Gallery of Infomania, a display of cities engaged in knowledge-based forms of development. Next, we will visit a heroic landmark in the information city: the Valley of Social Hopes. This valley is the enormous gap between two distant positions. One stands for the dreams of human liberation and enlightenment that continue to be nurtured by hopes for more intelligently guided technological advances. The other is the common and dominant myth that self-propelled, market-driven technological innovations in and by themselves are good for social progress. And finally we will arrive at the forum of ideas about how to control the direction and speed of technological change and urban development, and how to adapt both to support the needs of healthy communities, and the quality of cities.

1   Ten thousand years of urban information systems

To say "information city" is to be redundant: cities have always been organised around the management of information. This fact in dominant parts of the Western world is steeped in archetypal biblical irony. At the height of Babylonian times, so goes the Scripture, God decided to deflate humankind's exaggerated self-confidence, which had been boosted by an absolute ease of data exchange, and expressed by that pretentious skyscraper, Babel Tower, also known as One Babel Plaza. The punishment for the pompous building was biblical indeed: first abysmally low tenancy rates, then a general collapse of the speculative tower market, finally demolition of the property by controlled implosion, followed by a proliferation of languages and a hopelessly scattered myriad of tribes and nations, with all its current consequences. This quintessential Judaeo-Christian tale casts our unflagging attempts at lubricating information exchange in a tragicomic light — are we perhaps trying to rebuild that mythical tower?

Described here is an essential aspect of early cities. The very formation of cities and citadels — in Mesopotamia, the Indus Valley, Egypt or China — has brought about a proliferation of techniques for conveying societal messages through both shape and adornment of the built environment. So, along with the other great advances in handling communications and information: writing, mathematics, money and other accounting systems, we also find innovations in city architecture, as the means of storing and displaying information — and of moving it, by transporting and assembling people more efficiently, and more effectively. The dense networks of roads, public places, institutions and buildings that characterise the traditional city were largely arranged to produce, control and dispense intelligence and knowledge, in other words, processed, value-added information.

Discourse was immediate, mouth-to-ear, one-to-one, and between the few and the many. We should remember that today a very large — and not necessarily shrinking — portion of the world's population still communicates primarily in this way.

2   The city of print

With the reinvention of moveable type and the printing press half a millennium ago, the prospect of mass dissemination of stored information over great distances began to surface, and with it the slow erosion of the meaning of public space as a setting of social immediacy, and as the primary means of constructing and sharing reality. Today, the City of Print has us drowning in a sea of printed matter: books, pamphlets, newspapers, posters, billboards — and building facades themselves have long become a graphic medium.

3   Phone city

Roughly a century ago, the telephone, as the third major layer of cities' informational systems marked the beginning of environmental virtualisation in real time, in other words, the dematerialisation of live communications through the introduction of massive, largely urban, conduitry for telephony. This has added pure information encoded in modulated electric current to the other forms of conduit-channelled streams: people, goods, raw electricity, liquids and gases. It was also a century ago when rail-based transport went under way. Together, the railroad and the telephone helped bring about the puzzling phenomenon of simultaneous urban concentration and dispersal.

4   Broadcast city

Next came the age of conduit-free, centrally generated and mass-consumed electromagnetic transmissions: first radio and then television, roughly half a century ago. The layering notion still holds: neither mode of mass dissemination of information has displaced print, and both have probably had a boosting effect on printed products. The spread of television coincided with the final disintegration of the traditional city, and actually contributed to it with the introduction of televised lifestyles and a television-inspired mass consumer culture. Especially in the United States and Australia, the glorification of suburbia and the automobile was used to sell us wanton urban sprawl, banking on a process that could overnight transform cheap ex-urban land into a profitable commodity. New media, enhanced telephony, proliferating cars and air travel continue to support at once expansive and contractive forms of urbanisation.

The 20th century, the era of the mass media, has revealed the human settlement process as one of global mass consumption of the environment. Along with it, we witness a world-wide and much more pervasive version of the age-old contesting and re-colonising of existing cultural space. And this has resulted in the annihilation, displacement, and distillation of built cultural difference — that is, its evaporation and re-condensation. Coherent urban realms are engaged in a rampant process of dissipation, later re-crystallising as a kind of urban fallout, in unpredictable ways. They reincarnate, seemingly at random, as disjointed fragments of familiarity, and are re-assembled on a worldwide matrix of communication infrastructures. We all know such familiar fragments: urban islands such as shopping malls, business parks, or historic districts; the shrinking shreds of nature reserves; the living museums of extinction that we call zoos; the ubiquitous theme parks (our real virtuality): all floating in the global stew of our growing urban wastelands.

5   The new information city

And now, growing electronic capability has helped bring about a fifth era, vastly enhancing information exchange within and among industries. It appears to help accelerate global sprawl, further articulate a hierarchy of cities in the context of a global economic restructuring process and transform the dominant urban production regime into a world-wide assembly line, with a heavy concentration of managerial services in global nodes (Sassen 1991). A glance at the skyline of, say, Hong Kong, shows one physical implication of the recent expansion in the sheer quantity of information that is being processed in this regional agglomeration of the global money industry. New skyscrapers bloat in the eutrophic waters of international financial currents, absolutely dwarfing their brethren of only a few years ago.

But besides these rather casual results of economic and geographic trends, we find also a series of deliberate attempts to create urban settings whose very essence centres on advanced telecommunications and information technology. The 1980s saw a wave of highly visible initiatives presented under labels such as Information City, or even more ambitiously, Intelligent City. The notion of an information-suffused city using telematic technologies surfaced more than 20 years ago in both the United States and in Japan, where the information city was hailed as the home of the advanced information society, a phrase popularised by the

172

Japanese Ministry of International Trade and Industry (MITI). In the United States it began with the wired city ideas and the social hopes pinned onto the mere technical potential of broadcast television evolving into interactive broadband cable (Dutton, Blumler & Kraemer 1987).

It is striking how much the pre-1970s social engineering dreams of urban renewal resembled those of the city wiring efforts. Both predicted the elimination of social ills, urban prosperity and peace, democratisation and modernisation — not dissimilar to the espoused aims of the pre-Second World War Garden City movement.

Many of today's information cities still offer the warm aspirational glow of equal access, but only barely disguise a coolly pragmatic drive for competitive advantage. Overt attitudes vary widely: the countries of the European Union (EU), for example, show a range of region-specific approaches. More inspirational themes can be found among Italy's informatisation efforts, such as Naples' regional Città Cablata initiative, or Turin's inner-urban Lingotto building, the revitalisation of the former Fiat facility into a cultural resource. More pragmatically presented are the French projects or the smattering of thematic developments in Germany, such as Cologne's Media Park.

It is instructive to think of the North American and Japanese approaches as instances on opposite ends of a spectrum. Whereas in the United States city-based programs have been scrapped altogether and a path of an aggressively privatised wiring of the nation has been embarked on, Japan approached the subject with a veritable avalanche of programs, triggered by a host of ministries promoting highly information-serviced housing and industrial developments, with the optimistic aim to diffuse urbanisation away from Tokyo. If this policy has had an effect on regionalisation, it certainly has not been the one that planners had hoped for: the primacy of Tokyo has intensified, not stabilised, or even receded.

As an expanding summary, the following urban phenomena can be associated more or less directly with new information technology:

1. the so-called Information or Intelligent City initiatives: a wide range of experiments with both wired and wireless modes of information conveyance, providing electronic services, such as public communications; security; health; education; new modes of employment, including telework and tele-monitored work; shopping and banking; city governance and management; planning and modelling; environmental monitoring; traffic control; and the networked servicing of intelligent buildings;

2. economic development initiatives, in anticipation of, or response to new industrial models that are intrinsically information-oriented;

3. geographical phenomena, such as an accelerating trend towards total urbanisation and the emergence of world or global cities;

4. communities of electronic network users: telecommunities, computer tribes and other denizens of cyberspace;

5. the relatively recent genre of looking at urban space and buildings as informational entities, that is, in terms of image, expression, legibility, intelligibility and computable motion: as a few examples, remember aspects of the work of Lewis Mumford (1961a); Donald Appleyard (1973; Appleyard et al 1964); Kevin Lynch, (1960, 1972, 1976); Umberto Eco (1975, 1976), Doreen Nelson (1972); Venturi, Izenour and Rauch (Venturi et al 1972); Richard Wurman (1971); and Bill Hillier (1984); and

6. the final crisis of the disciplines of architecture and physical planning has received an added momentum. The traditional art of physical design, instead of reasserting its rooting power, is very much in danger of being relegated to a very insignificant role in the expanding, increasingly non-physical information space.

II Tales of a Few Cities

An increasing number of cities and towns strive for competitive advantage in ways that much more resemble the behaviour of large corporations and less that of the settled communities we are still used to. And when we look at the slogans and the plans with which cities have recently pursued their competitive growth strategies, we are struck by their very similarity, and the fact that many of the new themes are derived from the production and brokerage of knowledge. Indeed, a good deal of the current global interest in the future of cities is coloured by the interdependent changes in global economic structures, cultural realities and technological capabilities. Let me give you a few examples.

The Australian Multifunction Polis (MFP) concept has been an ambitious plan by the Australian and Japanese governments to build some form of new city, an urban construct designed to serve many purposes — hence the awkward name. The two countries had very different ideas about this. The sights of the Japanese partners were trained on leisure and so-called lifestyle opportunities, the vastness of the Australian continent, the climate, the beaches, and the relatively healthy conditions. For Australian governmental and industrial interests, hopes were pinned on manufacturing a global city. The idea was to attract international investment in nine areas considered to be 21st century industries, in a way that would amplify existing Australian strengths in these fields, and respond to Asia-Pacific and global markets. Key to all this was going to be a powerful information and telecommunications infrastructure — and the related industrial changes being witnessed throughout East Asia and Asia-Pacific.

Target industries included: art, culture and leisure; biotechnology; education; environmental management; health; information technology; media and communications; space engineering/transportation; and tourism. To package these industrial aspirations into an appealing concept, a characteristically post-industrial theme was chosen: "environment, humanity and technology". It was meant to express a desire to "put Humpty-Dumpty back together again", and to help fuse a fragmenting world. The dream was to foster a setting of creative complexity, where serendipitous synergies could thrive, and where three urban identities were integrated: a "Biosphere City", a city somehow in harmony with nature, a "Renaissance City" of culture and leisureful learning, and a "Technopolis" of research and development in advanced fields, and served by advanced infrastructures. And as it is typical for the age of the neo-liberal, virtualised metropolis, its regional administration is extraordinarily fragmented, with the new MFP administration emerging as a vital regional player — and potentially moving into the void. It remains to be seen if it will muster the institutional *chutzpah* to take charge in the subregional affairs of Adelaide's northwest quadrant.

The MFP concept, despite the human and ecological ambitions, was from the outset necessarily preoccupied with the wealth-creating possibilities of new technology, despite some policy wavering to the contrary over the years. The 1980s, however, did feature parallel initiatives that showed considerable concern with its social implications. The city of Kawasaki, sandwiched between Tokyo and Yokohama and an inseparable part of the great Tokyo-Osaka linear conurbation, was once famous for heavy industry, pollution, the water trade and stout workers' solidarity. It found itself in a maelstrom of industrial change, to electronics, services and other information industries. In the mid-1980s Kawasaki's former planning staff embarked on a two-pronged strategy. One aim was to attract and package these new industries together with a multitude of government programs designed to foster information city development — in part also to polish the city's tarnished image. The other challenge was to worry about what all this change meant or could mean to its people. For the first strategy, the central station was renewed and information-oriented office and science parks were located in industrial wastelands and under-used railroad yards.

To confront the social challenge, the city embarked on a series of civic initiatives, such as a bolstered supply of citizen centres and musea, and certain public brainstorming events. For instance, during the late 1980s it played host to the so-called Campus City Competition, which asked how the new technologies could possibly help the city's identity, and at the same time ameliorate growing societal challenges, such as those of community fragmentation, a lost sense of purpose, direction and identity. But most interestingly, the competition concept sought to challenge established forms of education and the very nature of learning. The strategy proposed by the winning entry (Droege 1988) was to closely link the physical and the informational changes of that city, to develop new resources of place and belonging, of community culture, urban nature and those promised by new knowledge infrastructures. The fundamental idea was to make all citizens stakeholders in the city's future, and focus with equal conviction on the city's "head, hand and heart", on its intellectual, physical and spiritual values. This vision, too, largely remained a dream, for two reasons. For one, the lack of experience with bottom-up community planning models that was typical for Japanese cities at the end of the previous decade led to a crisis of government when even the carefully selected citizenry (the citizen salon of elite representatives; supposedly leading the rest of the population like *nezumi*, mice) raised some uncomfortable questions about the purpose of *informatisation* that the administration was not prepared and able to answer. Secondly, and in a stroke of exceedingly bad luck, the city's vice-mayor and planning director found himself at the brunt of the Recruit bribery scandal, which ultimately led to the extermination of the entire planning department and the terminal paralysis of the Campus City concept.

But there is also a good number of stories that are closer to the reality of most cities, stuck between rhetorical ambitions and locally largely uncontrollable geo-economical forces. Ironically, many confirm the societal dilemmas that had motivated the Kawasaki competition.

Jakarta, for example, casts the conflicts in an especially stark light, as it tries to respond to new investment pressures. The city is caught in a quagmire. On the one hand, its elite sees a need to rapidly accommodate volatile knowledge industries: the inner-urban machines of the regional financial system, and information-industrial manufacturing facilities. On the other hand, a great deal of time, attention and skill is desperately needed to secure the viability of small and medium-size businesses and the existing, so-called informal sector, as well as its habitat. Bangkok's elite technocrats aspire to be global city planners, too. They are co-opted into a maelstrom of change, prodded on by international aid organisations and purveyors of infrastructure services of all kinds. These planners are unable and unwilling to even slightly buffer, no, in fact wish to magnify the impact of geo-economical and urban structural change. Here hi-tech development is waged like the Gulf War: a no-contest urban mayhem, with the two differences that the victims are allowed to reincarnate in a faraway outland, and that the manufacture of a new urbanity is the ultimate objective of operations, preferably in an aptly, neo-colonial faux classicism.

Amsterdam has had a colourful history as a thriving global city of the colonial kind. Today, it searches for technological roads to a new future, which to some planners spells state-of-the-art information infrastructures and industries, and a revitalisation of the financial services sector. Others see in these aspirations a threat to a cherished lifestyle, the destruction of a picturesque countryside, and an undermining of the relative resilience of a diverse economy. Amsterdam has managed to sidestep the question of urban change and accommodated new investment while maintaining a physical distinction between the old and the new Amsterdam, the centre and the periphery, between what has been called the "city of place" and the "city of flow" (Castells 1992), the two cities shaped by past and present forms of globalism and a very different logic of city building. Today, through an effort to compete with its own periphery and to shore up the inner city economically, the old city could be threatened by a waterfront redevelopment scheme "going global", in a frenzy of misplaced ambitions. Predictably, the current redevelopment plan is packaged into a knowledge and communications theme.

Boston uses its knowledge infrastructure to compete with its own hinterland for tax revenue. It attempts to strengthen the inner city as a newly attractive industrial location, with a downtown technopolis of knowledge-industrial facilities: biotechnology research labs, offices and hotels to be built atop its major train station. The project is a typical example for the literal translation of hoped-for technological opportunities into a physical plan.

Some people claim that the force of modern communications has brought about the fall of the wall in Berlin. As an immediate consequence of this event, the city faced great challenges of communicating between two deeply entrenched development administrations, and two very different sets of infrastructures. Today, the urge of attracting and accommodating new industries and jobs in the very heart of the city, and primarily in information-oriented industries, has spawned hopes for a new type of urban factory: lighter and smaller, stacked and camouflaged, decentralised and automatic. Such knowledge-based factories are envisioned in integration with more inner-city housing. The idea is that such solutions would limit the spectre of sprawling industrial zones at the city's periphery, and the environmental stranglehold of low-density residential ex-urbs.

Paris, with untiring vigour and unsurpassed showmanship, pursues its illustrious tradition of progressiveness that is today seen as requisite in the wooing of institutions and businesses of European and global stature. Examples of such showroom projects in the city's informational infrastructure are: the Centre Pompidou, the City of Science and Industry at La Villette, the "communication gate" of the Grand Arch at La Defense and others. These Grand Projects serve to convey the city and its aspirations, both in plain graphic articulation, and by spatially and functionally facilitating cultural discourse.

At the eve of a borderless, regionalised Europe the cities, again come into focus. There are at least two major EC initiatives worth mentioning: large programs to boost both basic research and applications in information technology and telecommunications, (with several initiatives targeting transportation and other urban systems) — and attempts to salvage the rapidly deteriorating urban environment. This effort particularly is likely to gain from new telecommunications and information-technological applications, such as pollution modelling and monitoring, and public communication methods.

Finally, there is the city and the country that pursues a tandem globalisation and IT (information technology) strategy with perhaps the highest degree of commitment and coordination: Singapore, and its IT 2000 plan. Here a young but rapidly growing governmental body, the National Computer Board (NCB), has over the past ten years pursued a nation-wide program to provide the fundamental segments of its industrial, cultural and urban life with the opportunities that computerisation and advanced telecommunications may hold, in a country that has no other indigenous resources than its own people. The agency grew to a staff of a thousand over the decade of its existence, and became in part responsible for sustaining the city's status as the world's largest container port by innovating expert system-based freight handling and processing systems and procedures. It divided Singapore's society and economy into a good dozen sectors ranging from education, transport and construction to leisure and tourism and scrutinised these in teams of young, enthusiastic yet earnest administrators to assess their potential scope of being computerised. IT 2000 was in 1992 elevated to a National Priority Project by Prime Minister Goh, during a celebration of NCB's tenth anniversary.

In summary, this is how the informatisation theme has related to cities and their competitive strategies. It has lent itself to bold, high-visibility themes, triggered calls for clear community development linkages, raised concerns over too rapid rates of change, highlighted the need for renewed social vision, to preserve existing cultural assets, facilitated flagship projects in attempts to strengthen ailing inner cities, led to the construction of tangible and sometimes useful icons of progress, generally lived most happily with an administrative machinery in flux or creative turmoil, has served many among the government's rank-and-file who are committed to vital issues.

While the basic development dilemmas are fairly well recognised, and it actually looks like we have the technological ingredients for urban regeneration — it is still very unclear at this point if and how these cities will be able to deal with new and vexing technology-driven challenges, of which there are two kinds: new manifestations of old power struggles and new challenges to the quality of cities in particular, but also more generally to the quality of life and the established societal regime at large.

To explain some of these challenges, it is useful to take a brief and polemic look at the one area that is perhaps most fundamentally affected by the new conditions: the workplace. To be sure, far from everyone is affected by these changes. Nevertheless, those impacts that can be described are symptomatic for larger dilemmas. Also, while technological changes admittedly may directly affect only a relatively small group of people, they do have an impact on a much larger population, in less tangible ways.

III   Barriers to a Better World

As with most other public policy issues, the goals of technological innovation in the urban environment, especially at the workplace, are ambiguous: a basic example is the ancient tension between the urge to control society in ever more intricate ways and the human desire to be without constraints, to be free. The paradoxical drive to increase both level of control and the number of options is as old as urban life itself, and here lies the root of our ideas about work. Cities have always functioned as information processors, cultural incubators, and giant work houses: machines designed to confine their subjects into workplaces and regiments. But people have also always been searching for ways of freeing themselves from oppressive working conditions, to assert a softer, more human nature, perhaps recalling the earlier, relatively paradisical state of matriarchal village life.

This dilemma continues to our time. In Europe and the United States we most clearly associate it with the last great era of technological change, the Industrial Revolution. Thomas Jefferson, third United States president, found himself in this very quandary, seeking to shape the nature of work in the face of innovation. In musing about intelligent forms of productivity, he much preferred pastoral peace and tranquility to the kind of industrialisation that England began to embrace in those days. "Let our work-shops remain in Europe", he wrote in 1785.

But the reality of workplaces was shaped by other forces. Industrialists like Daniel Webster saw a Manifest Destiny in new technology, to conquer nature, and societies deemed more primitive. He praised precisely the sort of working environments and technologies that promised high productivity through the logic of the machine. The idea was epitomised in Frederick Taylor and Henry Ford's accomplishments, and the expressions Taylorism and Fordism still connote both the benefits and costs of scientific work management and automated production (Marx 1987). Technological faith spread in this century, especially at times of heightened concern with national defence. Today, despite fiascos and disputes, most people still equate technological innovation with societal progress. As a result, many of us have difficulties envisioning other futures than the sort of clean techno-dreams that optimistic urban engineers like to engage in.

What does this mean to our workplaces? Why should we bother to look for alternative futures? Let us play the devil's advocate. The arrival of the new information technologies has triggered dreams of a soft, humanly managed world of ubiquitous, virtual places of enlightenment, networked into a Global Village. Will these dreams come true, or are the workplaces of the future going to be more like cages without walls, constructed in a mutant, digital form of Taylorism, or the neo-Fordism of societal automation: ever more refined, decentralised, multinational, and, well, automatic — that is to say, of a world that is moving the process of automation from simple production, distribution and administration to the overall management of the market at large (Hepworth & Robins 1988). To be more clear, let me examine information technology-related workplace dilemmas in four categories: space, time, quality and form of work.

1 Information Technology (IT) and the space of work

In spatial terms, many countries have seen a greater mobility of workplaces and production facilities. This has sped up urban sprawl, deepened dependence on the motorcar and fossil fuel, and challenged indigenous cultures, economies and ecologies. This global process is reinforced by structural transformations in many regional economies, and the footloose nature of international capital in this telematic age. It results in the new hybrid regions of Southeast Asia, where, for instance, untold specimens of a new foreign plant have invaded Thai rice fields over the past few years. One finds the same picture in Malaysia, Indonesia or the Philippines, and often with disastrous effects on the quality of cities and of work conditions alike. But we should also take a glance at the 18 new so-called cities that have recently mushroomed in the region of the United States capital, Washington DC, providing the cheap sort of R&D (research and development) space, conference and commercial facilities that are typical of post-industrial society. There is a tendency to segregate the work force by dividing operations into headquarter, front-office functions in the inner city, and back-offices or information labour camps in deep suburbia. And some observers report a clear trend towards new cottage industries, both as the new lifestyle of an information elite working at home, and the grimmer prospect of the home sweatshop for the less privileged.

2 IT and the time of work

Parallel to the softening of spatial boundaries, there is a corresponding dismantling of the traditional temporal structure regulating work. Yes, there can be greater freedom in choosing work hours, but this new work mobility across time and space — boosted by beepers, car radios, laptop computers, modems and proliferating networks — also means that we now have fewer reasons not to work at all times. Similarly, IT-facilitated productivity incentives such as decentralised competitive work units, ironically often result in longer, not shorter work hours under the stress of internalised incentives rather than external enforcement.

3 IT and the quality of work

IT brings liberties to the well-educated and mobile, and they are quite exciting, especially the promise of virtual work space or the interactive travel in educative information worlds — but under present conditions, that is, without supportive institutional innovations, they are inaccessible to the unskilled and financially and information poor. While

IT workplaces are theoretically conceivable as enlightening and empowering settings, they can really be less than stimulating, even inhumane. Actually, most jobs in an IT culture are vulnerable to both open and indirect surveillance, threatening cherished qualities such as trust, and depriving workers of their dignity and pride (Marx & Sherizen 1986). Moreover, IT can be an agent in the evaporation of economic systems supporting middle and lower ranks of the work force.

4   IT and the form of work

The most significant, yet most elusively IT-related, future development may be the merger of work, leisure, education and consumption into a single, digital life form. As consumers in our increasingly monitored societies we actually produce, on-line and in real time, highly detailed and dynamic data streams, informing the nature and direction of production. Education is on its way to becoming less fundamental and more application- and work-minded: see the rise of career-oriented pre-schooling, re-schooling and corporate training. And leisure emerges as a prospering industry, promulgating a clear work ethos in an age of increasing individual competitiveness, where non-productive leisure seems like a waste of time.

There is a fundamentally ambiguous quality in all of this: promises of a better life can lead to disappointments, if there is no clearly shared understanding of both intentions and impacts. We now know what the malaise of urban globalisation feels like: the signs of the global city syndrome range from steep land price rises to social fragmentation and cultural alienation (Sassen 1991). On the other hand, the actual technologies that help bring about this change theoretically do offer a certain enabling potential on a wide societal scale, and make conceivable wholly unprecedented ways of developing forms of knowledge that could prove to be vital to our collective survival.

However, very few of these great technical potentials will be realised automatically. They will require public commitment, broad, generous and flexible strategies, the willingness to take risks, and most of all, lots of experiments, rigorous research and open discussion. So, as the final feature of this small excursion, let us summarise some of the critical elements to be considered in building a humanely sustainable information city. There are three important social and physical ingredients required: a continuing and escalating struggle for the distribution of political power, now more important than ever; vitally enhanced levels of popular literacy, not simply in the use of advanced tools, but more critically in grasping the key changes transforming our communities, and the dynamics and challenges driving these; and the need to clearly structure urban investment in ways in which especially the oldest informative layers find physical articulation. What, then, are some of the detailed elements of these three innovation frontiers?

A key response to this POLIS *(power-literacy-structure)* challenge are balanced relations of power:

1. We need to encourage diverse and fine-grained economic and social functions. There is no insignificant industry, economic activity or social group. And there is a direct analogy to natural ecologies: higher diversity means broader economic vitality and social empowerment.

2. We must diffuse access. Uncommon efforts must be undertaken by government and industry to broadly distribute knowledge access to all parts of society, in wholly unprecedented ways.

3. We must innovate institutional structures. While it is important to secure identity and continuity of place and socio-economic patterns, it is equally important to deconstruct established oppressive institutions: there is a danger that a hardwiring, a technological freezing of anachronistic conditions will occur.

4. We have to end the myth that innovation is the same as progress. Technological innovation does not automatically spell social improvement, although most of us have come to believe so. Ways must be found to clearly subordinate the direction of technological change to social values and shared aspirations.

5. And we must make information rights an issue of the quality of life — and hence of the competitiveness of cities and companies. Just like cities compete with one another in infrastructural terms, they also ought to be made to compete in the ways in which they facilitate access through the technologies of knowledge.

The second element of this strategy is to build technological literacy. Let us:

1. publicly shape clear social goals in technological innovation, especially in the organisation and quality of work;

2. sponsor research and experiments that address all quality-of-life impacts of IT-inspired change;

3. foster deep institutional innovations to match the technological promise of popular enlightenment;

4. redefine educational objectives and restructure programs. For example, we ought to intelligently soften formal learning structures.

Lastly, let us:

5. nurture and guard independent realms of lifelong education that are profound, broad and, in the best sense of the word, political.

The third and stabilising element of this global approach is to reshape the structure and form of cities.

1. We now know how important it is to anchor memory in place. Local identity and territory for established communities and new groups is of absolute importance along with oases of transience.

2. We must nurture cities as information ecologies on all levels of their performance: the purposeful nature and communal fit of their spatial form, their graphic reading and their public networks.

3. We have to prepare technologies to prepare for inevitable and possibly beneficial forms of slow and even negative economic growth.

4. We have to prepare organisational, transport and other technologies to slow down or even reverse urban expansion on open land at the metropolitan fringe — even in times of seemingly high economic growth — by organically concentrating livable space in and around city and regional centres.

And last but not least, we must:

5. pursue planning control measures to civilise all investment energy into opportunities to enhance the physical, "high-touch" vitality, accessibility and intelligibility of urban places and cities.

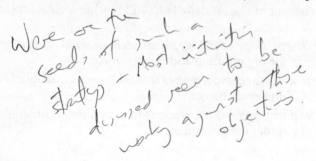

References

"A new vision for Canberra" 1992, *The Community Times*, 29 Apr, [An advertising supplement to *The Canberra Times*].

Allen, M 1994, "See you in the city!: Perth's cityplace and the space of surveillance", in *Metropolis Now : Planning and the Urban in Contemporary Australia*, (eds) K Gibson & S Watson, Pluto Press.

Anderson, AD 1977, *The Origin and Resolution of an Urban Crisis: Baltimore, 1890-1930*, Johns Hopkins University Press.

Anderson, B 1983, *Imagined Communities: Reflections on the Origin and Spread of Nationalism*, Verso.

Appleyard, D 1973, *Berkeley Environmental Simulation Laboratory : Its use in Environmental Impact Assessment*. Berkeley: Institute of Urban and Regional Development, University of California.

Appleyard, D, Lynch, K & Myer JR 1964, *View From The Road*, MIT Press.

Arrow, K 1962, "The economic implications of learning by doing", *Review of Economic Studies*, 29: 155.

Arrow, KJ 1984, *Collected Papers of Kenneth J Arrow, vol 4, The Economics of Information* , Blackwell.

Audley, D 1983, "Sydney's horse bus industry in 1889", in *Sydney's Transport: Studies in Urban History*, (ed) G Wotherspoon, Hale & Iremonger.

Australian Council of Trade Unions/Trade Development Council 1987, *Australia Reconstructed*, AGPS.

Australian Ratings Industry Profile (ARIP) 1991, *Retailing*, Sept.

Bate, W 1993, *Life After Gold: Twentieth-Century Ballarat*, Melbourne University Press.

Beder, S 1989, *Toxic Fish and Sewer Surfing*, Allen & Unwin.

Benedikt, M (ed) 1991, *Cyberspace: First Steps*, MIT Press.

Beniger, JR 1986, *The Control Revolution: Technological and Economic Origins of the Information Revolution*, Harvard University Press.

Benko, G & Dunford, M 1991, "Structural change and the spatial organisation of the productive system: An introduction", in *Industrial Change and Regional Development*, (eds) G Benko & M Dunford, Belhaven Press: 3.

Boyer, R 1988, *The Regulation School: A Critical Introduction*, Columbia Press.

Boyle, J 1992, "A theory of law and information: Copyright, spleens, blackmail, and insider trading", *California Law Review*, 80: 1416.

Braham, P 1985, "Marks and Spenser: A technological approach to retailing", in *Corporate Strategies for New Technology*

Braman, S 1989, "Defining information: An approach for policy makers", *Telecommunications Policy*, 13: 233.

Braudel, F 1981,*Civilization & Capitalism 15th-18th Century: The Structures of Everyday Life*, Fontana.

Breheny, M (ed) 1992, *Sustainable Development and Urban Form*, Pion.

Brindle, RE 1970a, "Calibration of an opportunities model for residential development", in *Analysis of Urban Development: Proceedings of the Tewksbury Symposium*, (ed) NF Clark, University of Melbourne Department of Civil Engineering, Transport Section Special Report no 5.

Brindle, RE 1970b, "The effects of transport improvements on urban development: Tests on an opportunities model", University of Melbourne, Department of Civil Engineering, Transport Section Special Report no 6.

Brindle, RE 1992, "Transport and land use: A 'neo-modern' approach", *Proceedings 16th ARRB Conference*, Part 6: 111, Vermont South, Victoria, Australian Road Research Board.

Brindle, RE 1994, "Trading off – or just shifting deck chairs?", *Proceedings of the 17th ARRB Conference*, 17(1): 161, Vermont South, Victoria, Australian Road Research Board.

Brotchie, J, Newton, P, Hall, P, & Nijkamp, P (eds) 1985, *The Future of Urban Form: The Impact of New Technology*, Croom Helm.

Business Review Weekly (various issues).

Butler, R 1993, Business opportunities for implementation of water re-use and reclamation programs, Paper presented to Effective Water Resource Management and Reform IIR Conference, Sydney, 13-14 Aug.

Butler, RE 1988, "Deregulation in the 1990s", *International Telecommunications Union*, 8 March.

Butlin, NG 1964, *Investment in Australian Economic Developement 1861-1900*, Australian National University Press.

Butlin, NG, Barnard, A & Pincus, JJ 1982, *Government and Capitalism: Public and Private Choice in Twentieth Century Australia*, George Allen & Unwin.

Butlin, SJ 1953, *Foundations of the Australian Monetary System 1788-1851*, Melbourne University Press.

Camilleri, J, Holmes, D, Huxley, M, James, P, Roberts, A, & van Moorst, H 1991, The Multifunction Polis: A city of contradictions, Submission to the Community Consultation Panel (MFP), Melbourne, 19 July.

Camilleri, JA & Falk, J 1992, *The End of Sovereignty? The Politics of a Shrinking and Fragmenting World*, Edward Elgar.

Cannon, M 1964, *The Land Boomers*, Melbourne University Press.

Cannon, M 1975, *Life in the Cities*, Nelson.

Cardew, RV & Simons, PL 1982, "Retailing in Sydney", in *Why Cities Change*, (eds) RV Cardew et al, Allen & Unwin.

Carter, R 1987, *The Information Technology Handbook*, Heinemann.

Cartwright, TJ 1991, "Planning and chaos theory", *Journal of the American Planning Association*, 57(1): 44.

Castells, M 1989, *The Informational City: Information Technology, Economic Restructuring, and the Urban-Regional Process*, Blackwell.

Castells, M 1992, *European Cities, the Informational Society and the Global Economy*, Centrum voor Grootstedelijk Onderzoek, Amsterdam.

Census of Victoria 1861, 1891.

Chanaron, J-J 1989, "French science policy and local high tech industries", *Science and Public Policy*, 16(1): 19.

Chapman, P 1974, "Energy costs: A review of methods", *Energy Policy*, 2: 94.

Clark, NF 1972, What about transport?, *Report of Proceedings of the Seminar on 'Planning Policies for the Melbourne Metropolitan Region'*, *Monash University*, 26 Feb, Melbourne and Metropolitan Board of Works: 20.

Clark, R 1992, Innovative management strategies, Paper presented to "Innovations in the Water Industry" IIR Conference, Sydney, 23-24 Nov.

Clingermayer, JC & Feiock, RC 1990, "The adoption of economic development policies by large cities: A test of economic, interest group and institutional explanations", *Policy Studies Journal*, 18(3), Spring: 539.

Coates, JF 1982, "New technologies and their urban impact", in *Cities in the 21st Century*, (eds) G Gappert & RV Knight, Sage Publications.

Commonwealth Census 1921, 1947.

Commonwealth Scientific and Industrial Research Organisation (CSIRO) 1991-92, Submission no 57 to the Industry Commission Inquiry into Water Resources and Wastewater Disposal.

Commonwealth Yearbooks .

Condit, CW 1988, "The two centuries of technical evolution underlying the skyscraper", in *Second Century of the Skyscraper*, (ed) LS Beedle, Van Nostrand Reinhold Company.

Conrads, U 1970, *Programs and Manifestoes on 20th Century Architecture*, Lund Humphries.

Cornell, A 1993, The smart money's now on EFTPOS, *The Australian Financial Review*, 14 Dec.

Cowan, HJ 1977, *Science and Building*, Wylie Interscience.

Coward, DH 1988, *Out of Sight. Sydney's Environmental History 1851-1981*, Department of Economic History, ANU, Canberra

Cronin, FJ, Parker, EB, Collerau, EK & Gold, MA 1991, "Telecommunications infrastructure and economic growth: An analysis of causality", *Telecommunications Policy*, 15: 529.

Cronin, FJ, Parker, EB, Collerau, EK & Gold, MA 1993, "Telecommunications infrastructure investment and economic development", *Telecommunications Policy*, 17: 415.

Cronon, W 1991, *Nature's Metropolis: Chicago and the Great West* , WW Norton & Company.

Dahmén, E 1988, " 'Development blocks' in industrial economics", *Scandinavian Economic History Review and Economy and History*, 34(1): 3.

Daniels, P 1991, "Producer services and the development of the space economy", in *The Changing Geography of Advanced Producer Services*, (eds) P Daniels & F Moulaert, Belhaven Press: 135.

David, A & Wheelwright, E 1989, *The Third Wave: Australia and Asian Capitalism*, Left Book Club Cooperative.

David, PA & Steinmueller, WE 1991, "The impact of information technology upon economic science", *Prometheus*, 9: 35.

Davidson, FG & Stewardson, BR 1974, *Economics and Australian Industry*, Longman.

Davison, G 1970, "Public utilities and the expansion of Melbourne in the 1880s", *Australian Economic History Review*, 10: 169.

Davison, G 1978, *The Rise and Fall of Marvellous Melbourne*, Melbourne University Press.

Davison, G 1987, "The capital cities", in *Australians 1888*, (eds) G Davison, JW McCarty, & A McLeary, Fairfax, Syme, & Weldon Associates.

Davison, G 1993a, "The past and future of the Australian suburb", Urban Research Program Working Paper no 33, Jan, ANU.

Davison, G 1993b, *The Unforgiving Minute: How Australians Learned to Tell the Time*, Oxford University Press.

Debresson, C 1989, "Breeding innovation clusters: A source of dynamic development", *World Development*, 17(1): 1.

Derry, TK & Williams, TI 1960, *A Short History of Technology*, Oxford University Press.

Dingle, T & Rasmussen, C 1991, *Vital Connections: Melbourne and its Board of Works 1891-1991*, McPhee Gribble.

Dodgson, M & Rothwell, R (eds) 1994, *The Handbook of Industrial Innovation*, Edward Elgar.

Dosi, G 1984, *Technical Change and Industrial Innovation*, Macmillan.

Doucet, MJ & Weaver, JC 1985, "Material culture and the North American house: The era of the common man, 1870-1920", *Journal of American History*, 72: 560.

Dowrick, S 1992, Policy implications of the New Growth Theory, Report for the Department of Industry, Trade and Commerce, Canberra.

Dowrick, S 1993, "New theory and evidence on economic growth and their implications for Australian policy", *Economic Analysis and Policy*, 23(3): 105, Sept.

Droege, P 1988, Technology for people, Grand Prix winning entry, International Concept Design Competition for an Advanced Information City, Kawasaki, Japan, in *Information Systems for Government and Business*, United Nations Centre for Regional Development (UNCRD).

Dunstan, D 1984, *Governing the Metropolis: Politics, Technology and Social Change in a Victorian City: Melbourne 1850-1981*, Melbourne University Press.

Dunstan, D 1985, "Dirt and disease", in *The Outcasts of Melbourne*, (eds) G Davison, D Dunstan & C McConville, Allen & Unwin.

Dutton, WH, Blumler, JG & Kraemer, KL (eds) 1987, *The Wired City*, GK Hall & Co.

Eco, U 1975, *Trattato di Semiotica Generale.*, Bompiani.

Eco, U 1976, *Segno*, Milano, ISEDI.

Economist, The 1990, 15 Dec: 16.

Economist, The 1991, 24 Aug: 30.

Economist, The 1993, 16 Oct: 92.

Ergas, H 1987, "Does technology policy matter?", in *Technology and Global Industry: Companies and Nations in the World Economy*, (eds) BR Guile & H Brooks, National Academy of Engineering Series on Technology and Social Priorities, National Academy Press.

Falk, J & Brownlow, A 1989, *The Greenhouse Challenge:What's to be done?*, Penguin.

Falk, J, Russell, S & Parker, K 1992, "New industries, sustainable development and the clever country" *Urban Futures*, Special Issue 5, Feb: 76.

Farrer, KTH 1980, *A Settlement Amply Supplied: Food Technology in Nineteenth Century Australia*, Melbourne University Press.

Fellows of the Australian Academy of Technological Sciences and Engineering 1988, *Technology in Australia 1788-1988: A Condensed History of Australian Technological Innovation and Adaptation During the First Two Hundred Years*, Australian Academy of Technological Sciences and Engineering, Melbourne.

Fisher, PMJ 1984, "Assessing economic impact in the Australian retail industry: Some extra-spatial considerations, an examination of the institutional setting for the introduction of new technology", in *Assessing the Economic Impact of Retail Centres*, (eds) R Stimson & R Sanderson, AIUS Publication no 122, Canberra

Fiske, J 1989, *Reading the Popular*, Unwin Hyman.

Fitzgerald, S 1987, *Rising Damp: Sydney 1870-90*, Oxford University Press.

Forester, T 1992, The electronic cottage revisited, *Urban Futures: Issues for Australian Cities*, Special Issue 5, Feb.

Freeman, C 1974, *The Economics of Industrial Innovation*, Pinter.

Freeman, C & Lundvall, B-A (eds) 1988, *Small Countries Facing the Technological Revolution*, Pinter.

Frost, L 1982, Victorian agriculture and the role of Government 1880-1914, PhD thesis, Monash University.

Frost, L 1990, *Australian Cities in Comparative View*, McPhee Gribble Penguin.

Frost, L 1991, *The New Urban Frontier: Urbanisation and City-Building in Australasia and the American West*, New South Wales University Press.

Frost, L 1992, "Government and economic development: The case of irrigation in Victoria", *Australian Economic History Review*, 32: 47.

Frost, L 1993, "Cities and economic development: Some lessons from the economic history of the Pacific Rim", in *Historical Analysis in Economics*, (ed) GD Snooks, Routledge.

Frost, L & Dingle, T 1993, Sustaining Suburbia: An Historical Perspective on Australia's Urban Growth, Paper to Urban Research Program Workshop on Urban Growth, September.

Frost, L & Jones, EL 1989, "The fire gap and the greater durability of nineteenth century cities", *Planning Perspectives*, 4: 333.

Gardner, C & Sheppard, J 1989, *Consuming Passion: The Rise of Retail Culture*, Unwin Hyman.

Giannopoulos, GA & Curdes, G 1992, "Innovations in urban transport and the *influence on urban form: An historical review", *Transport Reviews*, 12(1): 15.

Gibbs, DC 1992, "The Main Thing Today Is — Shopping: Consumption and the Flexibility Debate", Spatial Policy Analysis Working Paper no 15, Jan, School of Geography, University of Manchester.

Glaeser, E, Kallal, H, Scheinkman, J & Shliefer, A 1991, "Growth in Cities", Working Paper no 3787, National Bureau of Economic Research, Cambridge, MA , July.

Glatz, H & van Tulder, R 1989, Ways out of the international restructuring race?, Project proposal, Annex B, University of Amsterdam.

Gleick, J 1987, *Chaos: Making a New Science*, Viking.

Goldberg, ED (ed) 1977, *In the Sea*, John Wiley & Sons: 799.

Golledge, RG 1984, "Overview of shopping centre and other retail developments: Past history and problems of the 1980s", in *Assessing the Economic Impact of Retail Centres,* (eds) R Stimson & R Sanderson, AIUS Publication no 122, Canberra

Gorgeu, A & Mathieu, R 1992, "Developing 'partnerships': New organisational practices in manufacturer supplier relationships in the French automobile and aerospace industries", in *Reworking the World: Organisations, Technologies and Cultures in Comparative Perspective,* (ed) J Marceau, W de Gruyter: 172.

Greig, AW 1991, "Technological change and innovation in the clothing industry: The role of retailing", *Labour and Industry,* 3(2&3), June/Oct.

Greig, AW 1992, "Rhetoric and reality in the clothing industry: The case of post-Fordism", *The Australian and New Zealand Journal of Sociology,* 28(1): 45.

Habraken, NJ 1972, *Supports: An Alternative Approach to Mass Housing,* translation by B Valkenburg, Architectural Press.

Handy, S 1992, "Regional versus local accesibility: Neo-traditional development and its implications for non-work travel", *Built Environment,* 18(4): 253.

Hansen, W 1959, "How accessibility shapes land use", *American Planning Institute Journal,* 25: 73.

Hardy, AP 1980, "The role of the telephone in economic development", *Telecommunications Policy,* 4: 278.

Harris, B 1961, "Some problems in the theory of intra-urban location", *Operations Research,* 9: Sept-Oct.

Harris, R 1988, "American suburbs: A sketch of a new interpretation", *Journal of Urban History,* 15: 98.

Harris, TG 1993, "The Post Capitalist Executive: An interview with Peter Drucker", *Harvard Business Review,* 71(3): 116, May-June.

Headicar, P 1991, "Urban transport planning – will the regional pressures prove too great?", *Transportation Planning Systems,* 1(2): 3.

Headrick, DR 1981, *The Tools of Empire: Technology and European Imperialism in the Nineteenth Century,* Oxford University Press.

Headrick, DR 1988, *The Tentacles of Progress: Technology Transfer in the Age of Imperialism, 1850-1940,* Oxford University Press.

Hepworth, ME 1989, *Geography of the Information Economy,* Belhaven Press.

Hepworth, M & Ducatel, K 1992, *Transport in the Information Age: Wheels and Wires,* Belhaven Press.

Hepworth, M & Robins, K 1988, "Electronic spaces: New technologies and the future of cities", in *Futures,* Butterworth-Heinemann.

Hillier, B & Hanson, J 1984, *Social Logic of Space.,* Cambridge University Press.

Hirsch, F 1977, *Social Limits to Growth,* Routledge & Kegan Paul.

Hoffman, D 1973, *The Architecture of John Wellborn Root,* John Hopkins University Press.

Hofmeister, B 1988, *Australia and its Urban Centres,* Gebruder & Borntraeger.

Holgate, MW, Kassas, M & White, GF (eds) 1982, *The World Environment 1972-1982,* A Report by the United Nations Environment Programme, Tycooly International Publishing Company.

Holland, JH 1988, "The global economy as an adaptive process", in *The Economy as an Evolving Complex System*, (eds) PW Anderson, KJ Arrow, & D Pines, Addison-Wesley: 117.

Hoover, E 1948, *The Location of Economic Activity*, McGraw Hill.

Housing Industry Association (1990), *Our Homes Towards 2000: 1990-1991 Edition*, (unpub).

Inside Retailing (various issues).

International Bank for Reconstruction and Development 1991, Urban Policy and Economic Development: An agenda for the 1990s, World Bank Policy Paper, The World Bank, Washington DC.

Jackson, KT 1985, *Crabgrass Frontier: The Suburbanization of the United States*, Oxford University Press.

Jacobs, J 1985, *Cities and the Wealth of Nations: Principles of Economic Life*, Vintage Books.

James, P (ed) 1990, *Technocratic Dreaming: Of Very Fast Trains and Japanese Designer Cities*, Left Book Club.

Jencks, C 1978, *The Language of Post-Modernism*, Academic Editions.

Johnston, M & Rix, S 1993, *Water in Australia*, Pluto Press Australia in association with the Public Sector Research Centre, University of New South Wales

Jonscher, C 1983, "Information resources and economic productivity", *Information Economics and Policy*, 1: 13.

Joseph, R 1986, Technology parks: A study of their relevance to industiral and technological development in NSW, Report to New South Wales Department of Industrial Development and Decentralisation, Sydney, Mar, appendix 1: 95.

Joseph, R 1987, Symbolic politics in the high technology debate in Australia, PhD Thesis, University of Wollongong.

Joseph, R 1990, "Silicon Valley myth and the origins of technology parks in Australia", *Science and Public Policy*, 16(6): 353.

Kateley, R 1988, "Demand for high rise housing in the United States", in *Second Century of the Skyscraper*, (ed) LS Beedle, Van Nostrand Reinhold Company.

Kelley, AC & Williamson, JG 1984, *What Drives Third World City Growth? A Dynamic General Equilibrium Approach*, Princeton University Press.

Kellogg, WW & Bretherton, FP 1986, "The changing health of our planet: Observing the earth from space", *EOS Transactions of the American Geophysical Union*, 67: 816.

Kelly, M 1978, *Paddock Full of Houses: Paddington 1840-1890*, Doak Press.

Kenney, M & Florida, R 1988, "Beyond mass production: Production and the labor process in Japan", *Politics and Society*, 16,(1): 121.

Kenworthy, J 1991, "The land use/transport connection in Toronto", *Australian Planner*, 29(3) Sept: 149.

Ker, IR 1991, "Myopia, blinkers and lateral vision in transport planning", in *Urban Consolidation Myths and Realities, Proceedings of the Division Annual Conference Seminar*, Belmont, WA, June, Australian Institute of Urban Studies Western Australia Division: 34.

Keynes, JM 1937, "Some economic consequences of a declining population", *Eugenics Review*, 29: 13.

King, A D 1984, *The Bungalow: The Production of a Global Culture*, Routledge & Kegan Paul.

Klaasen, LH 1990, "The urban dimension", in *Transport and Spatial Distribution of Activities*, Report of the 85th Round Table on Transport Economics, Newcastle, UK, European Conference of Ministers of Transport, Paris.

Knight, RV 1993, Sustainable development – sustainable cities, *International Social Science Journal*, 135: 35-54.

Kristensen, P 1991, When labour defines business recipes — The Danish metal working industry cut off from corporate control and co-operation of local networks, Paper for the 10th EGOS Colloquium "Societal Change between Market and Organisation", Vienna, 15-17 July.

Krugman, P 1991, "Increasing returns and economic geography", *Journal of Political Economy*, 91(3).

Lack, J 1986, "McKay, Hugh Victor", in *Australian Dictionary of Biography Vol 10: 1891-1939*, Melbourne University Press.

Lamberton, DM (ed) 1971, *Economics of Information and Knowledge*, Penguin Books, Harmondsworth.

Lamberton, DM 1984, "The economics of information and organization", in *Annual Review of Information Science and Technology*, vol 19, (ed) ME Williams, American Society for Information Science: 3.

Lamberton, DM 1993a, "Globaloney: The impact of regions on the future of emerging markets in information technology and trade", *Pacific Telecommunications Review*, 14: 3.

Lamberton, DM 1993b, "The information economy revisited", in *Information and Communication in Economics*, (ed) R Babe, Kluwer, Dordrecht: 1.

Lamberton, DM 1994, Information and organization: Questions and clues, Paper prepared for the Third International Information Research Conference, Poigny la Forêt, France, [to be published in Proceedings], Saur.

Larke, R 1991, Japanese retailing: The view inside and out, Paper presented at the Fourth APROS International Colloquium, UMDS, Kobe, Japan, 25-28 June.

Lay, MG 1992, *Ways of the World*, Primavera Press.

le Corbusier 1964, *The Radiant City*, [translated by P Knight, E Levieux & D Coltman], Faber & Faber.

le Corbusier 1971, *The City of Tomorrow and Its Planning*, [translated by Etchells], MIT Press.

Leijonhufvud, A 1989, "Information costs and the division of labour", *International Social Science Journal*, 120: 165.

Lloyd, CJ 1988, *Either Drought or Plenty: Water Development and Management in NSW*, Kangaroo Press in association with the Department of Water Resources.

Lloyd, C, Troy, P & Schreiner, S 1992, *For the Public Health: The Hunter District Water Board 1892-1992*, Longman Cheshire.

Lucas Jr, R 1988, "On the mechanics of economic development", *Journal of Monetary Economics*, 22, July: 3.

Lundvall, B-A (ed) 1992, *National Systems of Innovation*, Pinter.

Lynch, K 1960, *Image of the City*, Technology Press.

Lynch, K 1972, *What Time Is This Place?* Cambridge, MIT Press.

Lynch, K 1976, *Managing the Sense of a Region*, MIT Press.

Macdonald, S, 1995 "Learning to change: An information perspective on learning in the organization", *Organization Science*, 6(2): 1-12.

Machlup, F & Mansfield, U (eds) 1983, *The Study of Information: Interdisciplinary Messages*, Wiley.

Mair, A, Florida, R & Kenney, M 1988, "The new geography of automobile production: Japanese transplants in North America", *Economic Geography*, 64(4): 352.

Manning, I 1984, *Beyond Walking Distance: The Gains from Speed in Australian Urban Travel* , ANU Press.

Manning, I 1991, *The Open Street*, Transit Australia Publishing.

Marceau, J 1990a, "Neither fish nor fowl: Theorising emerging organisational forms in a small open industrial economy", CIRCIT Working Paper Series, 1990/2.

Marceau, J 1990b, Oiling the wheels: Technological change and development in the automotive industry in Australia, (unpub). Urban Research Program, Australian National University.

Marceau, J 1992a, Globalisation, "glocalisation" and the creation of a new regional territory: Technological change and industrial restructuring in Australia, Paper presented to the International Sociological Association Research Committee 21 Meeting on "A New Urban and Regional Hierarchy? Impacts of Modernization, Restructuring and the End of Bipolarity", Los Angeles, 23-25 Apr.

Marceau, J (ed) 1992b, *Reworking the World: Organisations, Technologies and Cultures in Comparative Perspective*, W de Gruyter.

Marceau, J & Jureidini, R 1992, "Giants and dwarves: Changing technologies and productive interlinkages in Australian manufacturing industry", in *Reworking the World: Organisations, Technologies and Cultures in Comparative Perspective*, (ed) J Marceau, W de Gruyter, Berlin & New York: 151.

Marschak, J 1968, "Economics of inquiring, communicating, deciding", *American Economic Review*, 58: 1 [reprinted in *Economics of Information and Knowledge*, 1971, (ed) DM Lamberton, Penguin: 37].

Marshall, A 1961, *Principles of Economics*, 9th edn, Macmillan.

Marti, J & Zeilinger, A 1985, "New technology in banking and shopping", in *The Information Technology Revolution*, (ed) T Forester, Basil Blackwell.

Marx, GT & Sherizen, S 1986, "Monitoring on the job", in *Technology Review*, MIT Press.

Marx, L 1987, "Does improved technology mean progress?", *Technology Review*, MIT Press.

MATS 1966, Metropolitan Adelaide Transportation Study, Progress Report, June, MATS Joint Steering Committee.

McCarty, JW 1970, "Australian capital cities in the nineteenth century", *Australian Economic History Review*, 10:107.

McKinsey & Company Management Consultants 1993, *Emerging Exporters*, Australian Manufacturing Council.

McLoughlin, B 1991, "Urban consolidation and urban sprawl: A question of density", *Urban Policy and Research*, 9(3): 148.

Mees, P 1995, "Toronto: Paradigm regained", *Urban Policy and Research* , 12(3): 146.

Meier, RL 1960, "Information, resource use, and economic growth", in *Natural Resources and Economic Growth*, (ed) JJ Spengler, Resources for the Future, Inc, Washington, DC.

Meier, RL 1962, *A Communications Theory of Urban Growth*, MIT Press, Cambridge.

Meier, RL 1980, *Urban Futures Observed in the Asian World*, Pergamon.

Meinig, DW 1962, *On the Margins of the Good Earth: The South Australian Wheat Frontier 1869-1884*, Rand McNally & Company.

Menou, MJ 1993, The impact of information on development: Results of a preliminary investigation, Paper presented at the Third International Information Research Conference, Poigny la Forêt, France.

Meyer, JR & Gómez-Ibáñez, JA 1981, *Autos Transit and Cities*, Harvard University Press.

Miller, GA 1983, "Foreword", in *The Study of Information: Interdisciplinary Messages*, (eds) F Machlup & U Mansfield, Wiley.

Mills, G 1992, Retailing practices and marketing power, Paper presented at the Conference on Industrial Economics, CEPR and Bureau of Industry Economics, ANU, Canberra, 16-18 July.

Mitchell, RB 1959, "Metropolitan Planning for Land Use and Transportation", The Office of Public Works Planning, The White House, Washington DC.

Mitchell, RB & Rapkin, R 1964, *Urban Traffic: A Function of Land Use*, Columbia University Press.

Mokyr, J 1990, *The Lever of Riches: Technological Creativity and Economic Progress*, Oxford University Press.

Morduch, J 1993, Book review, *Journal of Economic Literature*, 31: 931.

Morris, M 1988, "Things to do with shopping centres", in *Grafts: Feminist Cultural Criticism*, (ed) S Sheridan, Verso Press.

Moss, M 1983, Information cities: The example of New York City, Paper for Critical Issues on National Computerization Policy Conference, Honolulu.

Mouritz, M 1992, Catchment management approaches: The evolution of water sensitive design in Perth WA, Paper presented to "Innovations in the Water Industry" IIR Conference, Sydney, 23-24 Nov.

Moyal, A 1984, *Clear Across Australia: A History of Telecommunications*, Nelson.

Mullins, P 1981, "Theoretical perspectives on Australian urbanisation. I: Material components in the reproduction of Australian labour power", *Australian and New Zealand Journal of Sociology*, 17.

Mullins, P 1988, "Is Australian urbanisation different?", in *A Sociology of Australian Society*, 2nd edn, (eds) J Najman and J Western, Macmillan.

Mumford, L 1961a, *City in History: Its Origins, Its Transformations and Its Prospects*, Secker & Warburg.

Mumford, L 1961b, *The Town in History*, Secker & Warburg.

Muschamp, H 1993, Thinking about tomorrow and how to build it. *Times*, 10 Jan, Section 2: 1, 32.

Myrdal, G 1957, *Economic Theory and Under-Developed Regions*, Duckworth.

Neilsen, K 1991, "Towards a flexible future: Theories and politics", in *The Politics of Flexibility: Restructuring State and Industry in Britain, Germany and Scandinavia*, (eds) B Jessop et al, Edward Elgar.

Nelson, DG 1972, *Manual for the City Building Educational Program: Architectural Consultant Edition*. Washington DC: National Endowment for the Arts.

Nelson, RR 1980, "Production sets, technological knowledge, and R&D: Fragile and overworked constructs for the analysis of productivity growth?", *American Economic Review*, 70: 62.

Nelson, RR 1981, "Assessing private enterprise an exegisis of tangled doctrine", *Bell Journal of Economics*, 12: 93.

Nelson, RR (ed) 1993, *National Innovation Systems*, Oxford University Press.

Neutze, M 1981, *Urban Development in Australia*, Revised edition, George Allen & Unwin.

New South Wales 1990, Sydney: Hub of the Australian multifunction polis, NSW Government Final Proposal for the Joint Feasibility Study, Sydney, May.

Newman, P 1991, "Greenhouse, oil and cities", *Futures*, May: 335.

Newman, P 1992a, "Railway renaissance", *Habitat Australia*: 22.

Newman, P 1992b, "The compact city: An Australian perspective", *Built Environment*, 18(4): 285.

Newman, PW & Kenworthy, JR 1989, *Cities and Automobile Dependence: A Sourcebook*, Gower Press.

Newton, P 1991, "The new urban infrastructure", *Urban Futures*, Special Issue no 5.

Newton, P 1993, "Australia's information landscapes", *Prometheus*, 11: 3.

Nulty, T 1992, "Global perspectives", in *Telecommunications Management and Policy: Australian and International Perspectives*, (eds) A Bodi, A Newstead, & PB White, Monash University: 3.

Organisation for Economic Cooperation and Development 1991a, *The OECD Environment Industry – Trends and Issues*, DSTI/IND (91), 1 (Restricted): 197.

Organisation for Economic Cooperation and Development 1991b, *Environmental Change and Science and Technology Institutions — The Experience of Selected OECD Countries*, DSTI/STP (91) 22 (Restricted): 34.

Owens, S 1986, *Energy, Planning and Urban Form*, Pion.

Pawley, M 1991, *Theory and Design of the Second Machine Age*, Blackwell.

Pikusa, S 1986, *The Adelaide House 1836 to 1901: The Evolution of Principal Dwelling Types*, Wakefield Press.

Piore, R & Sabel, C 1984, *The Second Industrial Divide*, Basic Books.

Porter, MF 1990a, *The Competitive Advantage of Nations*, Free Press.

Porter, MF 1990b, "The competitive advantage of nations", *Harvard Business Review*, March-April.

Poulsen, M 1982, "Retail development", in *Why Cities Change*, (eds) RV Cardew et al, Allen & Unwin.

Prices Surveillance Authority 1987, "Inquiry in relation to retail prices of clothing", Report no 15, AGPS, Canberra.

Raban, J 1975, *Soft City*, Fontana.

Reekie, G 1993, *Temptations: Sex, Selling and the Department Store*, Allen & Unwin.

Reinecke, I 1982, *Micro-Invaders: How The New World of Technology Works*, Penguin Books.

Riemens, W & Marceau, J 1992 "Building blocks of the future: The new materials 'complex' in Australia", Background paper prepared for J Marceau (ed) *The Competitive Advantage of the Welfare State* [to be published in 1996].

Romer, P 1992, "Endogenous technological change", *Journal of Political Economy*, 98: S71.

Roobeek, A 1987, "The crisis of fordism and the rise of a new technological paradigm", *Futures*, April.

Sassen, S 1991, *The Global City*, Princeton University Press.

Saxenian, A 1991, "Local area networks: Industrial adaptation in Silicon Valley", in *Cities of the 21st Century*, (eds) J Brotchie, M Batty, P Hall & P Newton, Longman Cheshire: 275.

Sayer, A 1986, "New developments in manufacturing: The just-in-time system", *Capital and Class*, 30: 43-72.

Schroeder, J 1988, "Space-saving elevators for the very tall buildings", in *Second Century of the Skyscraper*, (ed) LS Beedle, Van Nostrand Reinhold Company.

Schumpeter, JA 1953, *History of Economic Analysis*, Oxford University Press.

Scott, A & Storper, M (eds) 1986, *Production, Work and Territory*, Allen & Unwin.

Selwood, J 1979, "Public transport and urban growth", in *Western Landscapes*, (ed) J Gentilli, University of Western Australia Press: 423.

Senker, J 1988, *A Taste for Innovation: British Supermarkets' Influence on Food Manufacturers*, Horton Publishing.

Shackle, GLS 1969, *Decision, Order and Time in Human Affairs*, 2nd edn, Cambridge University Press.

Shackle, GLS 1972, *Epistemics & Economics*, Cambridge University Press.

Shields, R (ed) 1992, *Lifestyle Shopping: The Subject of Consumption*, Routledge.

Simon, JL 1986, "Some theory of population growth's effect on technical change in an industrial context", *Australian Economic History Review*, 26: 148.

Sinclair, WA 1975, "Economic growth and well-being: Melbourne 1870-1914", *Economic Record*, 51: 153.

Singer, C (ed) 1954, *A History of Technology*, vol 4, Clarendon Press.

Soete, L 1991, Technology and economy in a changing world, Paper presented to the Conference on Technology and the Global Economy, OECD/Department of Industry, Science and Technology, Canada, Montreal, 3-6 Feb.

Sole, F & Valls, J 1991, "Networks of technological collaboration between SMEs: Strategic and spatial aspects", in *Innovation Networks: Spatial Perspectives*, (ed) R Camagni, Belhaven Press: 196.

South Yorke's Peninsula Pioneer 1900.

Swedberg, R 1990, *Economics and Sociology Redefining their Boundaries: Conversations with Economists and Sociologists*, Princeton University Press.

Sydney Water Board 1991-92, Submission to the Industry Commission Inquiry into Water Resources and Wastewater Disposal (includes appendix on Rouse Hill project).

Tarr, JA & McMichael, FC 1976, "The evolution of wastewater technology and the development of State regulation: A retrospective analysis", in *Retrospective Technology Assessment – 1976*, (ed) JA Tarr, San Francisco Press.

Tarr, JA & Dupuy, G 1988, *Technology and the Rise of the Networked City in Europe and America*, Temple Press.

US Information Infrastructure Task Force 1993, *The National Information Infrastructure: Agenda for Action*, NTIA.

van Huut, H 1991, The right business in the right place, PTRC Summer Meeting (vol P341), PTRC: 19th Proceedings Seminar A Vol P341 PTRC, Education and Research Service Planning and Transport Research and Computation International Association London.

van Tulder, R (ed) 1988, *Small Industrial Countries and Economic and Technological Development*, SICRA & NOTA, Amsterdam.

van Tulder, R & Junne, G 1988, *European Multinationals in Core Technologies*, John Wiley.

Venturi, R, Brown, D & Izenour, S 1972, *Learning from Las Vegas*. MIT Press.

Victorian Yearbooks

Wachs, M 1984, "Autos, transit, and the sprawl of Los Angeles", *Journal of the American Planning Association*, 50(3), Summer: 297.

Walmsley, DJ & HC Weinand 1991, "Changing retail structure in southern Sydney", *Australian Geographer*, 22(1): 57-66.

Webber M 1964, "The urban place and the non-place urban realm", in *Explorations in Urban Structure,* MM Webber, JW Dyckman, DL Foley, AZ Gutenberg, WLC Wheaton & CB Wurster, University of Pennsylvania.

Webster, FV, Bly, PH & Paulley NJ 1988, *Urban Land-Use and Transport Interaction: Policies & Models*, Avebury.

Weiss, L 1988, *Creating Capitalism: The State & Small Business Since 1945*, Blackwell.

White, C 1992, *Mastering Risk: Environment, Markets & Politics in Australian Economic History*, Oxford University Press.

White, R 1995, "The forbidden city: Young people and public space", no 15, *Arena Magazine*, February/March 15: 34.

Whitley, R 1990, "East Asian business systems & the comparative analysis of forms of business organisation", *Organization Studies*, 11(1): 47.

Whitley, R (ed) 1992, *European Business Systems*, Sage, [especially chapter 1 'Societies, firms & markets: The social structuring of business', pp 5-45].

Williams, M 1974, *The Making of the South Australian Landscape,* Academic Press.

World Commission on Environment and Development 1987, *Our Common Future*, Oxford University Press.

Wrigley, EA 1985, "Urban growth and agricultural change: England and the Continent in the early modern period", *Journal of Interdisciplinary History*, 15: 683.

Wurman, RS 1971, *Making the City Observable*, Walker Art Center and MIT Press

Young, L 1992, "Comfort and decency: Furniture and equipment in Adelaide homes", in *William Shakespeare's Adelaide 1860-1930*, (ed) B Dickey, Association of Professional Historians Inc.

INDEX